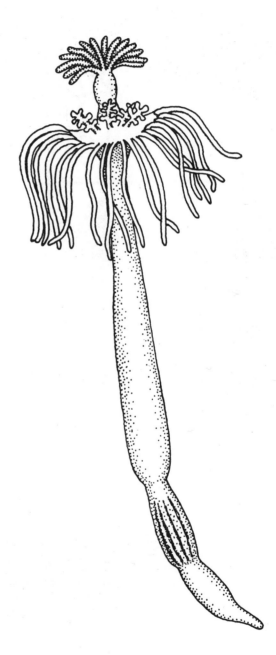

Invertebrate Identification Manual

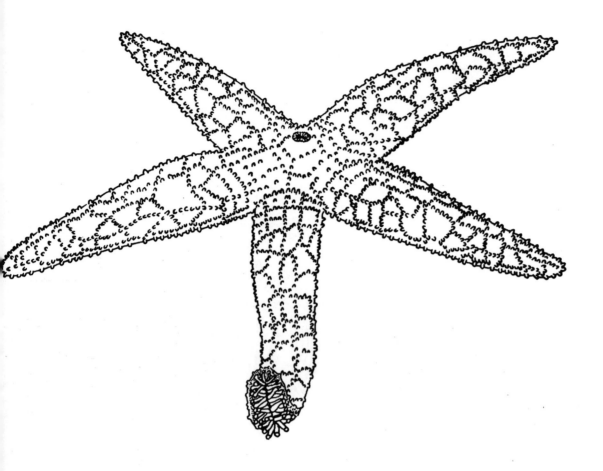

D. Van Nostrand Company
New York • Cincinnati • Toronto • London • Melbourne

Invertebrate Identification Manual

Richard A. Pimentel

Biological Sciences Department
California State Polytechnic College
San Luis Obispo, California

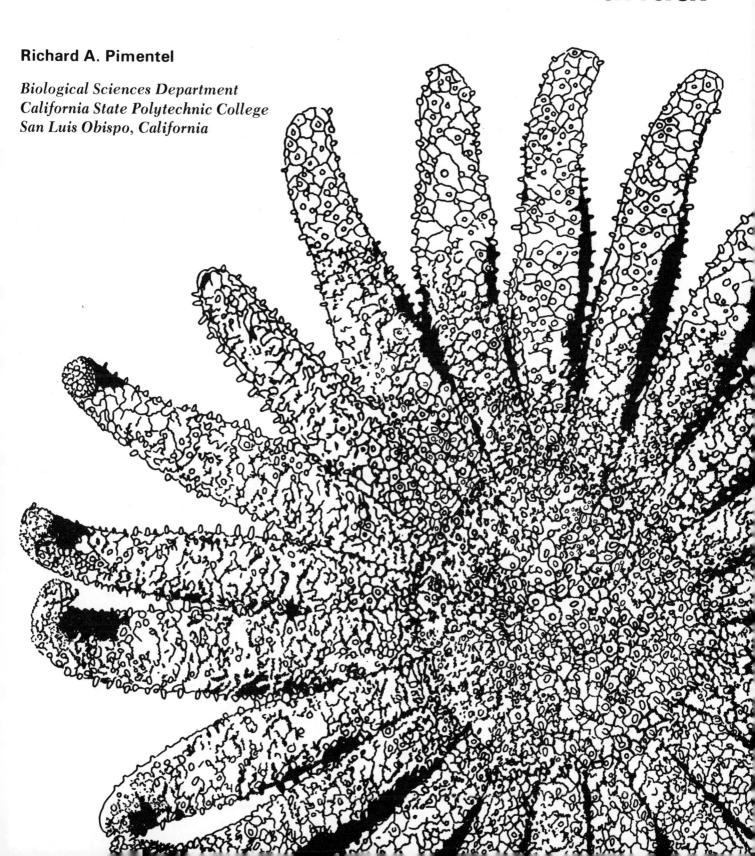

D. Van Nostrand Company Regional Offices:
New York   Cincinnati

D. Van Nostrand Company International Offices:
London   Toronto   Melbourne

Manufactured in the United States of America

Published by D. Van Nostrand Company
135 West 50th Street, New York, N.Y. 10020

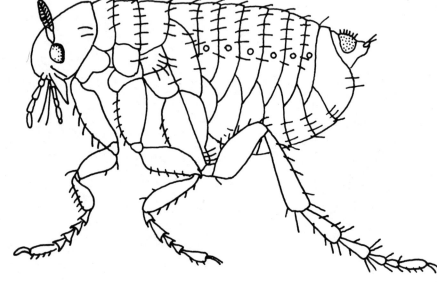

Preface

The purpose of this book is to aid and encourage an interest in invertebrates. Although specialists, including bird, mammal, insect, and shell biologists, can refer to manuals designed for their restricted interests, no previous volume identifies all of the adult land, water, and air invertebrates of North America.

Here, invertebrates are recognized as groups representing units of scientific classification. Some animals are diagnosed no further than very large classification categories, others to small units. While many scientific and technical terms are used for structures, common names are available throughout, since this is intended to be a nontechnical manual.

Both field biologists and amateur naturalists will find this book useful. Biologists will find that it helps to solve the problem of combining identification with other aspects of biology. Often, in courses conducted entirely in the field, such as natural history, field biology, limnology, ecology, marine biology, entomology, and invertebrate zoology, the instructor is forced to compromise between identification and other tools of instruction. For example, some compromise exists in field biology or ecology when identification provides insufficient recognition of kinds of organisms for meaningful comparisons between organisms and their environments. In other instances, the student is exposed essentially to one or the other, often owing to the text selected. For these reasons, some biologists have expressed the need for a nontechnical manual that identifies invertebrates in some depth. It is their belief, and mine as well, that such a manual would be a useful supplement to a main text that emphasizes aspects other than identification.

In my handling of the invertebrate program for the National Audubon Society at Audubon Camp of the West, my original belief that laymen would be interested in all invertebrates was justified. Their attention to animals and their natural history need not be limited, as it frequently is, to vertebrates, for once people are introduced to invertebrates, a new and fascinating world is uncovered. All that many amateur naturalists require is a key to this world.

A primary objective was to allow direct use of this manual by people with varying interests. For example, the brief material on identifying invertebrates indicates what is necessary for those satisfied only to name invertebrates. The remainder of the introduction, at least in part, matches the varying degrees of interest of those desiring more detailed study.

Richard A. Pimentel
San Luis Obispo, California
May, 1967

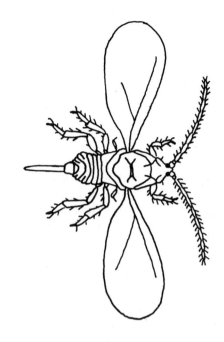

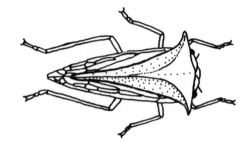

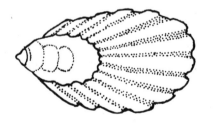

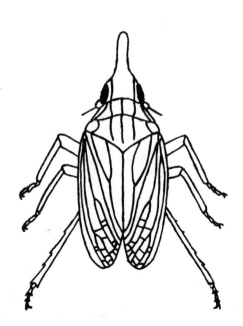

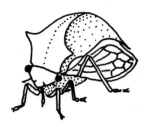

CONTENTS

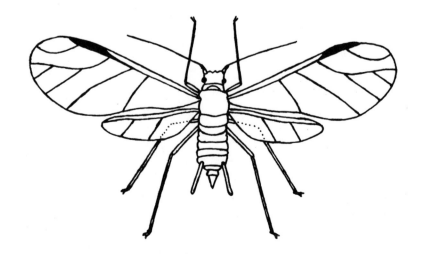

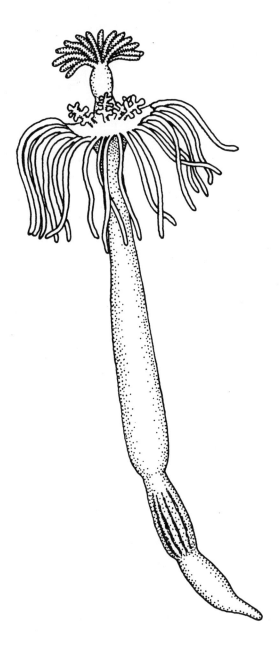

Invertebrate Identification Manual

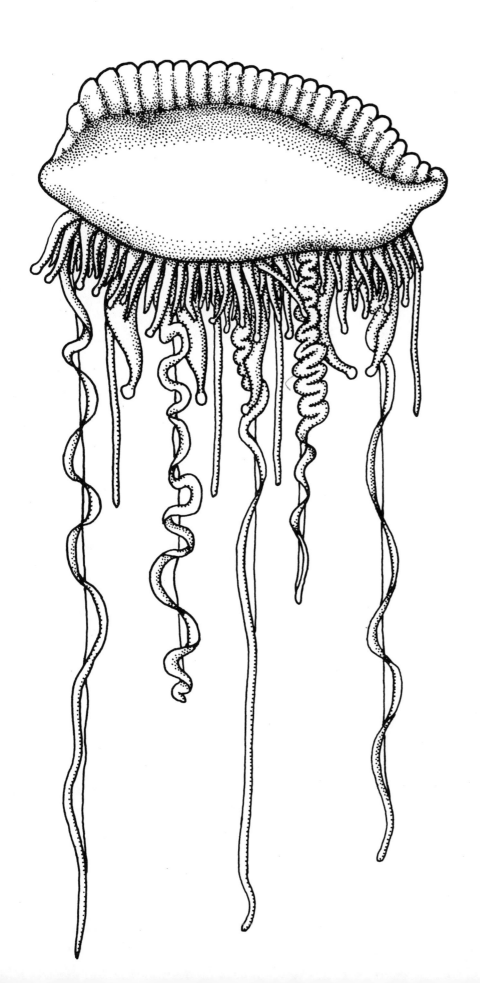

There are more than two million, perhaps even more than five million, species of invertebrates. The vertebrates, by contrast, comprise only about forty thousand species; they include the fishes, amphibians, reptiles, birds, and mammals—one subphylum, Vertebrata, of the phylum Chordata. Heretofore, no attempt has been made to identify all the North American invertebrates in a single volume. That is the objective here. In general, all adults of North American land, freshwater, intertidal marine, and parasitic forms are considered to some taxonomic level. Certain immature, subtidal marine, extralimital, and fossil groups are also included to demonstrate the wide variety of invertebrate forms.

COVERAGE

Since this book proposes to identify hundreds of thousands of species, obviously not all species are included. In fact, single species are seldom diagnosed. Rather, animals are grouped according to units of biological classification larger than the species, such as phylum, class, order, family, and rarely, group. Ultimate identification is therefore not balanced in the taxonomic sense.

The author offers no concise explanation for all his choices of smallest taxonomic unit recognized. However, certain loose criteria are followed. First, groups are separated to the point where there are no more simple differences in structure, that is, they are usually classified on the basis of gross external appearance. This separation generally follows biological classification.

Second, some of the smallest taxonomic units are omitted, and some uncommon families excluded. For example, in six orders of insects, the Hemiptera, Neuroptera, Coleoptera, Lepidoptera, Diptera, and Hymenoptera, certain rare families are not mentioned. Most so-called rare families that are occasionally or locally conspicuous are included.

Additional criteria for coverage are related to taxonomic custom and perhaps somewhat, to the author's bias. Taxonomic custom is based on the extent to which nonspecializing biologists tend to separate the animals.

ORGANIZATION

There are three facets to overall organization: biological classification, diagnoses, and illustrations. Biological classification provides a way of proceeding from the largest unit of classification, the phylum, through ever smaller taxonomic categories to the smallest one recognized.

Diagnoses are an intergral part of the biological classification. Each taxonomic category is usually described to allow its determination with the aid of only a 10x hand lens. However, identification requires more than an exposition of structure. Frequently, life cycle, habitat, and feeding habits are important criteria for diagnosis; hence,

they, and, occasionally, other details of behavior, are included. Therefore, although identification is stressed, general natural history is outlined as well. To accomplish all this in a reasonable amount of space, synoptic style became necessary.

Illustrations offer visual representations of many important diagnostic features of individual groups. However, neither figures nor written diagnoses are intended to be separate means of identifying invertebrates. Rather, illustrations and text complement one another as parts of an overall device.

Names

In spite of appearances, the dissemination of scientific names is not a purpose in itself. It is assumed that users of this manual might range from individuals wanting much detail to those wanting little. In order to allow the user to choose the extent and kind of names desired, both scientific and common names are found at all levels of classification for individual organisms, e.g., from phylum to family for many insects.

There are no outstanding innovations in nomenclature. Scientific names used and the categories they represent are accepted as conservative interpretations of existing knowledge by most invertebrate zoologists. Innovations, if they can be said to exist here, are found in the vernacular names. Although the vast majority of common names are in general use by biologists, some attempt is made to include those used by laymen. Also, in certain instances, especially where translations of scientific names appear meaningful, common names are proposed. Moreover, when alternate common names exist, many are given.

Scope of Identification

The organization of this manual allows the reader to decide the taxonomic level to which he will make identification. It is necessary to identify all organisms at least to phylum; this can be the end of identification. But since many animals can be traced down through subphylum, class, subclass, order and family, any one of these levels can be a stopping point.

Classifying, Studying, and Identifying

The remainder of the introduction contains three topics, "Biological Classification," "Studying Invertebrates," and "Identifying Invertebrates." Biological classification is discussed further because it is the basis of organization in this book. Next, "Studying Invertebrates" examines means of obtaining invertebrates and provides some suggestions for further work with them. Finally, "Identifying Invertebrates" suggests how to use the second part of this manual.

BIOLOGICAL CLASSIFICATION

Phylogeny is the study of the history of life, especially the evolutionary interrelationships and ancestry of living organisms. On the basis of our present knowledge of phylogeny, we can place living things into convenient categories or groups. In this section we will examine the methods by which organisms are classified into *taxonomic categories* and the method of naming those categories, *nomenclature*. Also, to understand the basis for classification of animals we must examine their complexity in reference to phylogeny.

CLASSIFICATION AND TAXONOMY

Since there are millions of species of living organisms in the world today, it is impossible for anyone to know all of them. Yet, for various reasons, man is a great labeler. He appears to have a passionate desire to name things, a characteristic that seems to obscure and all too often to satisfy his ignorance. Probably since the time of the earliest humans, names have been applied. Perhaps in order to simplify things and arrange them in his mind, ancient man attempted many schemes of classification.

Man's efforts to name organisms led to the science of taxonomy, the grouping of organisms. Early schemes were purely matters of convenience, using such things as habits and habitats to group animals together. According to that now-defunct system whales, seals, and porpoises would be grouped with fishes. Today, biologists do their best to determine animal *ancestry* and *relationships* and to use that information for purposes of classifying. In modern taxonomy, the whales, seals, and porpoises are classified with mammals. Even today, however, the complexity of known phylogeny may necessitate a classification of pure convenience; known evolution may be too intricate to be shown by modern or any relatively simple means of classification. In spite of this possibility, the modern biologists' attempts to use relationships to form groups have resulted in the most convenient, especially for learning and remembering, and most informative scheme to date.

Taxonomic Categories

The basic unit of taxonomy is the single kind of organism, or *species*. (The term "species" is both singular and plural; the word "specie" means coined money.) A species may seem to be a very definite thing. Everyone recognizes dogs, cats, cows, and horses as species because each group is unique and easily distinguished. However, these well-known animals present a warped view of conditions in nature. Perhaps the best way of contemplating a species is

to think of its existence in view of the death of many of its ancestors. For example, the African and Indian elephants are two similar but different species that are related through common ancestry; if time could be ignored and the ancestors and all intermediate types to these two species were living today, one would find it impossible to separate the elephants into two species. For this reason, if one considers the known possibility of two living, geographically isolated groups of organisms that possess similar form and habits, the problem of determining what is and what is not a distinct species can be appreciated. Although past life does not exist to create problems in species definition, some very closely related living organisms cause the same sort of difficulty. What then is a species? The common idea, gathered from the less complex kinds of species, is that a species is a group of organisms freely reproducing with one another but reproductively isolated from all other groups of organisms. For many purposes this is a satisfactory way of thinking of a species.

Categories above the species are strictly for convenience and may not be accepted by all biologists. For example, within a single family the number of genera recognized by different biologists may range from five to ten. This occurs because individual higher categories are never equivalent when applied to different groups, no matter how hard a biologist might try for uniformity. Uniform higher categories are impossible, because evolution does not produce units of distinct and discontinuous size; rather, the consequence of evolution is a continuous variation in the size and complexity of different units. In spite of this, larger categories are valuable when they represent natural groups; hence, the primary criterion for any of these larger groups is common ancestry and the larger the category, the more organisms are included. Similar species with common ancestry are grouped into *genera* (singular *genus*), genera into *families* (singular *family*), families into *orders*, orders into *classes*, classes into *phyla* (singular *phylum*), and phyla into *kingdoms*. Depending on the classification scheme, there are two kingdoms, Animalia and Plantae; three kingdoms, those two, plus Protista; or four kingdoms, the preceding three, plus Monera. It should be noted that botanists tend to use the term *division* instead of phylum.

Many categories below the species level may be recognized. However, only *subspecies* and *variety* have much use and meaning. The subspecies designation is restricted mostly to animal species. In its usual meaning it refers to a geographic race that has some structural or other difference from the rest of its species. A variety, a plant subunit of the species, can be a structural variant without regard to distribution, a structural variant forming a geographic race, a structural variant sharing the range of other variants of the same species, or a color or habit (form of growth) variant.

The species and other categories already mentioned are the basis of a framework within which one can start with a very large group, such as a phylum, and work down through finer groupings, all attempting to show relationship and usually assuming *common ancestry,* until the individual organism is distinguished. In some cases, and to obtain additional groups, the species and higher categories are further subdivided or grouped by the addition of the prefixes *sub-* and *super-* (respectively, something less than and something more than the group so designated). Also, *infra-* may be used as a unit just below *sub-.* The subspecies is an example of this type of division. Also, such categories as *tribe* and *variety* assume particular places in the heirarchy of biological classification. In certain detailed taxonomic studies special categories (e.g., cohort, brigade, legion, and section) are created and defined to fulfill special needs. These latter categories always must be defined, because they do not possess a standardized position in the taxonomic heirarchy.

An example of the categories generally used to classify modern man are as follows:

Kingdom Animalia
  Subkingdom Eumetazoa
    Phylum Chordata
      Subphylum Vertebrata
        Superclass Tetrapoda
          Class Mammalia
            Subclass Theria
              Order Primates
                Suborder Anthropoidea
                  Family Hominidae
                    Genus *Homo*
                      Species *sapiens*
                        Subspecies *sapiens*

Nomenclature

Nomenclature is the scientific naming of organisms. Scientific names for species (generally considered "the scientific name") are binomial, consisting of both the generic and specific names. Man belongs to the genus *Homo* and species *sapiens.* His scientific name, a combination of the generic and specific names, is *Homo sapiens.* Parenthetically we must avoid possible confusion. There are two meanings of "specific name." So far we have used this term to indicate a single word in a binomial. However, "specific name" also can mean "the binomial scientific name" of a species. For example, the specific name of man is *Homo sapiens.* Moreover, unless one is referring separately to binomial components, the scientific name always is two words.

When written or printed, scientific names must conform to certain set procedures. Notice that the generic name is capitalized and the second word is uncapitalized. This standard procedure is always followed in this book and is essential for animal designations. In addition,

specific names must be either underlined, italicized, or printed in boldface type. Often the last name, or an abbreviation of the last name, of the biologist who proposed the organism's name is appended to the scientific name, as in *Homo sapiens* L., the L. being an abbreviation of Carl von Linne ("Linnaeus"), who proposed the scientific name for man. Sometimes the biologist's name is included in parentheses; this means that there has been a change in the name originally applied (see "Name Changes" below). Finally, the names may come from Latin, Greek, or any other language, or have meaningless deriviation; however, all must be latinized, as *californica* or *californicus* for California and *washingtonii* or *washingtonia* for Washington. Higher taxa names have the same origin as specific names and are always capitalized but require no special printing or writing. The taxon designation is capitalized only when combined with a scientific name (e.g., Family Hominidae).

Name Endings

Certain larger taxonomic categories tend to have uniform endings because of rules for naming. Although exceptions to these rules are permitted on the basis of pre-rule common usage, the following taxa usually have the endings shown:

Superfamily	-oidea
Family	-idae
Subfamily	-inae
Tribe	-ini

Name Changes

In general, scientific names are quite stable. However there are circumstances under which scientific names can be changed. The two main sources of redesignations are *taxonomic revisions* and the *law of priority.* In part, the law of priority states that the first name given a species shall be its scientific name.

Changes due to taxonomic revision generally reflect scientific progress. They are based upon new interpretation of biological relationships as a result of study of one or more species. This can cause one or more of three possible name changes: (1) A species must be transferred from one genus to another, so the generic name becomes different. (2) It is discovered that what had been considered two species is a single species, so one specific name must be dropped, or synonomized, and the first given name be established for the species as a whole (law of priority). (3) What was thought to be a single species is found to be two or more species, in which case new specific names are given to each of the new species. All of these examples are "scientific changes of names."

Reassignments due to the law of priority alone are the common example of "nomenclatorial changes in names." These changes often are criticized because they do not stem from new knowledge or scientific progress. The technicalities in relation to the law of priority and to other bases for nomenclatorial changes in names are extremely complex. However, a simple example of a replacement according to the law of priority would involve a generic and/or specific name's being superseded because a properly and earlier applied name is found. In spite of the fact that these alterations do cause difficulty and exasperation, they are an aspect of the very thing that yields the great stability characterizing most scientific names.

Phylogeny

Animal Complexity

The trends in animal evolution were and are so many that the structural features of many species are extremely complex. Considering this complexity, it is fortunate that only a few anatomical and other characteristics are needed to separate the phyla and to indicate their possible paths of evolution. The five main features are grade of organization, embryology, symmetry, body cavities, and segmentation. In discussing them no attempt will be made to imply sequences of events. This is not necessary because the sequence of each is generally believed to be from the simple to the complex.

Grade of Organization

Animal organization, especially in the simpler types, is somewhat similar to that of plants. This is logical because plants and animals probably were derived from the protists. The first animals may have consisted of a single, multicellular body, but one with all cells much the same; in other words, they were cellular organisms. With time, animal structure became increasingly more complex. Cells became specialized in structure and function; cells of similar structure and function became grouped into tissues, tissues into organs, and finally, organs into organ systems. For this reason animals can be classified according to evolution of their organization as cellular, tissue, and organ system grades. Animals usually are not believed to display an independent organ basis of structure. However, there is sufficient peculiarity of flatworm (Platyhelminthes) structure for some zoologists to describe it as a complex of tissue, organ, and organ system organization, often termed "tissue-organ."

Embryology

Many features of embryonic development are important for understanding of evolutionary history, and for classification of living phyla. Here only the germ layers found in multicellular animals are reviewed. In development, the fertilized egg divides to form a ball of many cells, the *blastula*, which has a cavity, the *blastocoel*. Ultimately these many cells differentiate into two or three layers, *germ layers*, in a so-called gastrula stage. The germ layers probably are not strictly comparable in all phyla; however,

each germ layer forms certain body structures. The outer germ layer, the *ectoderm*, forms the nervous system and outer coverings of the body; the inner layer, the *endoderm*, forms the lining of the organs of the digestive system; the middle layer, the *mesoderm* (a layer sometimes absent), forms the skeleton, muscles, and circulatory system.

Symmetry

Many sponges are asymmetrical, as indicated by one's inability to divide them into two equal, or mirror-image, halves. Other Porifera are essentially *spherical* in their symmetry. A test of this is the ability to divide one of these animals into halves by any cut passing through the center of the ball-like form. The Coelenterata, Ctenophora, and Echinodermata have *radial* or *biradial* symmetry; however, that of echinoderms is a secondary evolutionary acquisition from bilateral forms as a result of a sedentary life. Radial symmetry is found in a pie, because an infinite number of cuts through the center and in one plane will produce two mirror images. Biradial symmetry can be likened to a pie with two cherries put on a diameter of the pie and at equal distances from the center. In biradial symmetry there are only two ways of cutting to produce equal halves, one through the centers of the pie and two cherries and the other through the center of the pie and perpendicular to the first possible cut. *Bilateral* symmetry is the commonest and most advanced type. It is found in most of the phyla. Only a single cut is possible if one is to form equal halves, or right and left mirror images.

Body Cavities

The Ectoprocta through the Chordata have true body cavities, or *coeloms*, of two types, *schizocoels* and *enterocoels*. The Mollusca and Arthropoda have reduced coeloms; their body cavity, the *hemocoel*, is so named because blood circulates through it. The Acanthocephala, Aschelminthes, and Entoprocta have so-called false body cavities, *pseudocoels*. Those animals lacking a body cavity are said to be *acoelomate*.

Segmentation

Segmentation is the linear repetition of body parts. True segmentation is conspicuous externally and internally in most Annelida; it is visible mainly externally in the Arthropoda, and internally in the Chordata. Especially in chordates, segmentation may be seen clearly only during development.

Miscellaneous Characters

The nature of other features, such as skeleton, appendages, and sexual status, are also important in diagnosing phyla. These biological aspects are described very briefly as they are used in the following classification of animals.

SYMMETRY

asymmetrical

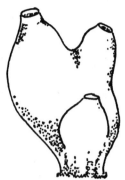

spherical

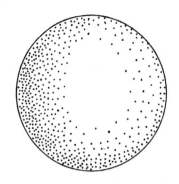

radial

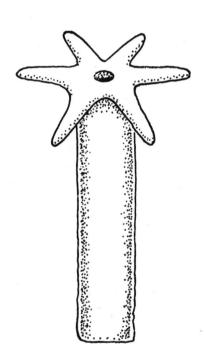

biradial

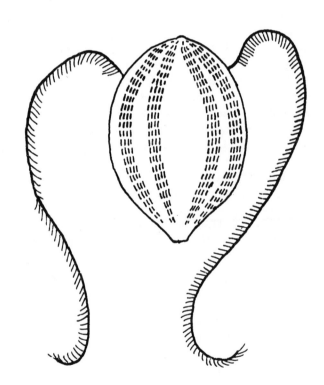

bilateral

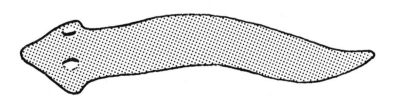

Animal Classification

The principles of animal complexity permit the separation of the animal phyla in different ways. A widely used classification (Hyman's) is that given below.

Kingdom Animalia—cellular, tissue, or organ system organization; multicellular animals

SUBKINGDOM MESOZOA—composed of an outer layer of body cells and an inner layer of reproductive cells; cellular organization

PHYLUM MESOZOA (Mesozoans)

SUBKINGDOM PARAZOA—cellular organization, but almost at the tissue level of organization

PHYLUM PORIFERA (Sponges)

SUBKINGDOM EUMETAZOA—tissue or organ system grade of organization

GRADE RADIATA—primarily of radial symmetry; tissue grade of organization with incipient organ systems and mesoderm

A. Symmetry radial, biradial, or essentially bilateral; mouth usually encircled by tentacles; no rows of ciliated plates

PHYLUM COELENTERATA (CNIDARIA) (Coelenterates)

B. Symmetry biradial; tentacles, if present, not encircling mouth; 8 rows of ciliated paddle-plates

PHYLUM CTENOPHORA (Comb Jellies)

GRADE BILATERIA—symmetry bilateral or secondarily radial; organ system grade of construction; mostly with mesoderm of ectodermal origin and usually with a body cavity other than the digestive cavity

A. Acoelomata—region between digestive cavity and body wall filled with cells; no body cavity

1. Anus absent, poorly developed organ systems, often considered tissue-organ organization

PHYLUM PLATYHELMINTHES (Flatworms)

2. Anus present, organ systems present

PHYLUM NEMERTINEA (RHYNCHOCOELA) (Ribbon Worms)

B. Pseudocoelomata—space between digestive tract and body wall incompletely lined by cells of mesodermal origin; space is a remnant of a developmental cavity, the blastocoel

1. Digestive tract absent

PHYLUM ACANTHOCEPHALA (Spiny-headed Worms)

2. Intestine essentially straight; anus posterior

PHYLUM ASCHELMINTHES (Cavity Worms)

3. Intestine looped; anus near mouth

PHYLUM ENTOPROCTA (Moss Animals)

C. Eucoelomata—body cavity a true coelom

1. Lophophorata—with a circular, crescent-shaped or double spiraled, coiled ridge (the *lopho-*

phore) bearing ciliated tentacles; intestine looped, bringing mouth near anus; body cavity a schizocoel.

a. Colonial, with gelatinous, chitinous, or calcareous encasements

PHYLUM ECTOPROCTA (BRYOZOA or POLYZOA) (Moss Animals)

b. Solitary

(1) Wormlike

PHYLUM PHORONIDA (Fan Worms)

(2) With a bivalve shell

PHYLUM BRACHIOPODA (Lamp Shells)

2. Schizocoela—coelom originates as a space in the mesoderm; no lophophore

a. Unsegmented

(1) Visceral mass covered by a body fold, the mantle, which secretes a shell; contains a small group having true segmentation.

PHYLUM MOLLUSCA (Mollusks)

(2) No mantle; naked; wormlike

(a) With an eversible proboscis

PHYLUM SIPUNCULOIDEA (Peanut Worms)

(b) Proboscis not eversible; mouth ventral

PHYLUM ECHIUROIDEA (Echiurids)

b. Segmented

(1) No jointed appendages

PHYLUM ANNELIDA (Segmented Worms)

(2) With jointed appendages

PHYLUM ARTHROPODA (Joint-legged Animals)

3. Enterocoela—coelom originates as pouches from the embryonic gut

a. With secondary, usually five-rayed, radial symmetry

PHYLUM ECHINODERMATA (Spiny-skinned Animals)

b. Bilateral symmetry retained throughout life

(1) Without gill slits or internal skeleton

(a) Without circulatory or excretory systems

PHYLUM CHAETOGNATHA (Arrow Worms)

(b) With both circulatory and excretory systems

PHYLUM POGONOPHORA (Beard Worms)

(2) With gill slits or internal skeleton or both

(a) Without typical notochord (internal skeletal rod) in adult or embryo

PHYLUM HEMICHORDATA (Acorn Worms)

(b) Embryo with notochord, gill slits, and dorsal hollow nerve cord; adults with gill slits or vertebral column or both

PHYLUM CHORDATA (Chordates)

STUDYING INVERTEBRATES

This section will prove helpful to those whose interest in invertebrates involves the capture of animals. It is mostly concerned with methodology, and includes the organization of field work, collecting equipment and procedures, rearing techniques, photography, and collections, topics that really are groundwork for study.

Coverage of methodology is not exhaustive, the objective here being to present an overall procedure that is sufficient for most purposes. However, selected references are given for those wanting more detailed information.

Various items of equipment, especially chemicals and collecting devices are discussed. Although many of these can be obtained locally or constructed, the names of biological supply houses, are provided as sources of materials.

ORGANIZING FIELD WORK

Field work must be organized; a haphazard approach will be reflected in poor results. However, highly organized collecting *per se* need not be the sole aim of the collector, and even the hobbyist should consider going further.

One need not be a professional to contribute knowledge. Serious amateurs have and will continue to contribute to natural history. If this becomes a goal, one should preserve specimens for verification of identification and other purposes, and record exact geographic locations, habits, and dates. Better still, one might expand records to include time of day, weather conditions, and any other aspect of an organism or locale that might appear significant.

The above objectives demand extreme care in keeping track of animals at all times during their handling and in recording field observations. A specimen without data is often worthless biologically, but data without a specimen can have scientific value.

Field Notebook

The key to obtaining a valuable collection, then, is the field notebook. The basic headings a notebook might contain for each field trip are date, locality, habitat(s), weather conditions, and collections. Collections should include many numbered subunits, each based upon some or all animals taken from a particular site under like conditions. In other words, a single collection number should refer to animals sharing identical data.

Collection numbers are especially useful. Assigned consecutively, they are applied to specimens throughout their handling and are necessary to supply complete and accurate data for collection labels. Moreover, all intermediate

"tagging" of specimens is by these numbers, thereby eliminating the need for many detailed intermediate labels.

Judgment is required in deciding when to terminate one collection number and when to start another. The basis for decision must always be, "Am I obtaining the details I need?" On occasions when data are minimal, a single collection number may apply to an entire day of collecting. However, if unlike habitats are explored or any other important change in information occurs, it will be necessary to change numbers.

The value of a field notebook as a source of knowledge cannot be overemphasized. Worth and effort tend to be synonymous. Records should be detailed rather than general. One should indicate, after each specimen, the exact site in which it was found rather than give a generalized record of habitat. Also, one might include observations on individual activity including feeding, reproduction, predation, locomotion mechanisms, etc.; on protective coloration, concealment, or conspicuousness; and on relative abundance.

Field Handling

When invertebrates are captured, they are placed in killing jars or containers such as vials, and field notebook records are made of these captures. Animals placed in a container are immediately tagged with a "collection number." However, only organisms having a single collection number are placed together into a single container or into the same killing jar, where they are kept separate from all other collections until dead. Dead invertebrates are transferred from the killing jar to a vial or pill box, their collection number going with them.

The above precautions result in properly tagged specimens that are represented in a field notebook by adequate data.

COLLECTING

Collectors can cause wholesale destruction to organisms and their environment. People not realizing the damage they were doing have in a few minutes destroyed much life in an area. However, organisms can be collected either as a hobby or avocation without jeopardizing life. This is accomplished by leaving habitats as they were found. Rocks and other moved objects should be put back as they were, and searches should never be concentrated to "favorite spots." Similar habitats are almost always available; one need not exploit a single locale at any one time and should not return to an area any sooner than is abso-

COLLECTING EQUIPMENT

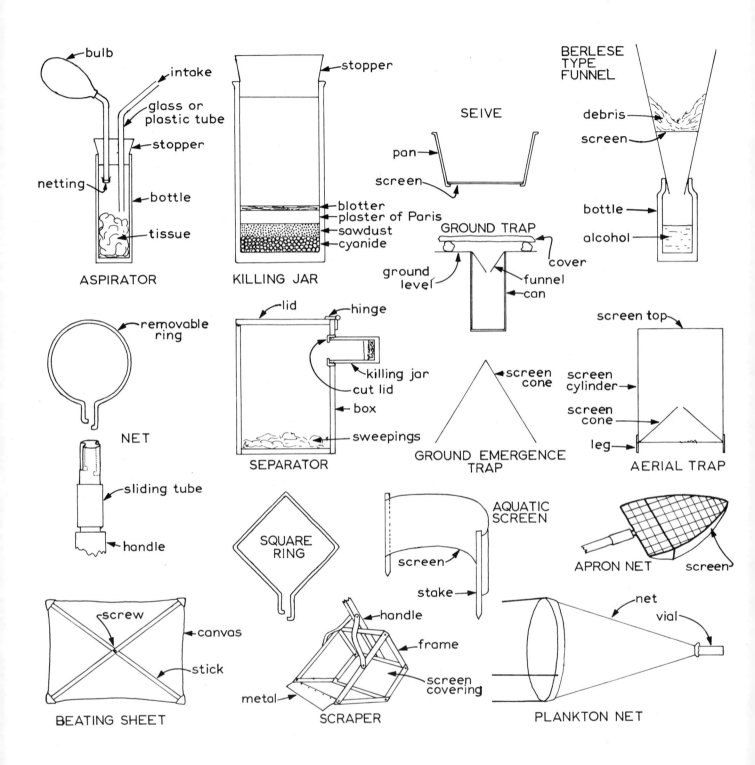

bulb

intake

glass or
plastic tube

stopper

netting

bottle

tissue

ASPIRATOR

stopper

blotter
plaster of Paris
sawdust
cyanide

KILLING JAR

SEIVE

pan

screen

GROUND TRAP

cover

ground
level

funnel

can

BERLESE
TYPE
FUNNEL

debris

screen

bottle

alcohol

removable
ring

NET

sliding tube

handle

lid

hinge

killing jar
cut lid

box

sweepings

SEPARATOR

screen
cone

GROUND EMERGENCE
TRAP

screen top

screen
cylinder

screen
cone

leg

AERIAL TRAP

SQUARE
RING

AQUATIC
SCREEN

screen

stake

handle

frame

screen
covering

metal

SCRAPER

APRON NET

screen

net

vial

PLANKTON NET

screw

canvas

stick

BEATING SHEET

lutely necessary. Obedience to these simple rules will demonstrate that removal of life for study need not be destructive.

Collectors limiting their take to one or a very few of each kind of organism, destroying an absolute minimum of habitat, and making every attempt to return a habitat to normal generally cause no serious damage to life or habitats. In fact, the collector who attempts to rectify what he knows was done may do less harm than the observer who believes he causes no damage.

Collecting Techniques

Obtaining knowledge of invertebrates does, of course, require the acquisition of many specimens. This naturally means that many locales and habitats must be examined and a variety of collecting methods used. We will now consider techniques in reference to broad habitats, terrestrial, freshwater, and marine. Although many procedures are introduced and equipment is emphasized, discussion is generalized—specialized and expensive procedures are ignored.

Prior to examination of terrestrial, freshwater, and marine collecting, features common to most collecting are considered. These include equipment, methods of using equipment, capture and/or removal of invertebrates, and imprisoning or killing.

Equipment

Collecting requires a wide assortment of devices. Whenever an item of equipment is necessary, if appropriate, it will be described, in sufficient depth for one to construct it. Equipment that is simpler to purchase, e.g., forceps, is not described.

Equipment Use

Some devices necessitate an explanation of their use. This will be given in the text.

Capture and/or Removal

Although equipment is frequently utilized to trap animals, trapping may not actually place specimens under complete control of the collector. For example, one may trap a scorpion, but still have to secure the animal in a container. Usually securing can be accomplished by using the hands, forceps or tweezers, an aspirator, or a small moist art or camel's hair brush. It is recommended that one employ a syringe bulb on an aspirator rather than use the mouth. Using a bulb prevents oral intake of minute invertebrates and especially eggs that may find a suitable habitat within man. To use an aspirator, the syringe bulb is squeezed, and the invertebrate is taken into the bottle as the bulb is released.

Emprisoning or Killing

Final treatment of invertebrates in the field generally involves placing them alive into a container or killing them.

Animals that are to be brought back alive usually can be placed in a plastic or cloth bag or bucket. Glass or metal buckets or jars are often both inconvenient and unsafe to carry into the field.

Animals that are best handled if killed in the field may be placed in preservative or a killing jar. For preserving, the collector may use small plastic screw top vials and jars of assorted sizes containing 80% alcohol (preferably reagent or ethyl alcohol), 5% formalin, or K. A. A. K. A. A. and killing jars require further explanation.

K. A. A.

This special liquid mixture often provides excellent killing and preparation for wormlike and other soft-bodied animals. It is a mixture of one part kerosene (coal oil), two parts acetic acid (glacial), and ten parts reagent (100%) or ethyl (95%) alcohol. The desirable effects of K. A. A. upon soft-bodied animals are rapid kill and penetration, plus some tissue inflation. The degree of inflation of specimens is related to the amount of kerosene used; hence kerosene might have to be reduced to as little as one-tenth part. The acetic acid retards darkening of specimens, and alcohol is the main preservative. Soft-bodied animals should be kept in K. A. A. until fully extended, at which time many specimens require further fixation in 70% alcohol or 5% formalin in preparation for placement in storage preservative.

Killing Jars

Under ideal circumstances, at least two killing jars, one about an inch in diameter and four to six inches long and the other about the size and shape of a one-pint, wide-mouthed peanut butter jar, are used. Cork stoppers are best for convenience in opening and closing, but a solid screw cap lid is satisfactory. Also, plastic jars are safer than glass. All killing jars using cyanide should be labeled "POISON." A cyanide killing jar, if broken, must, for safety's sake, be buried.

To transform empty bottles into killing jars, one of three killing agents, ethyl acetate and two cyanides, is usually used. Ethyl acetate, a liquid, is slower acting than cyanide, but its effect on invertebrates is likely to be more permanent than that of cyanide. To make an ethyl acetate bottle, a mixture of plaster of Paris and water is placed in the bottom of the jar and allowed to dry completely, then a few drops of ethyl acetate are added. A less satisfactory method is simply placing ethyl acetate on cotton or paper.

Calcium cyanide is placed on the bottom of the jar, then covered by a layer of cotton, and finally a cardboard disc is forced down upon the under layers. Potassium cyanide is usually tamped, covered by dry, tamped plaster of Paris, and finished with a layer of plaster of Paris and water. One should be careful *not* to make the plaster of Paris and water mixture too wet, a thick mixture being desirable.

A special killing jar should be restricted to moths and butterflies. Other invertebrates placed in a moth or butterfly killing jar become covered with scales and often make poor specimens.

Because killing jars can become overcrowded with specimens, it is often best to carry pillboxes and envelopes into the field. Pillboxes containing cleansing tissue serve as temporary storage for most dead invertebrates. Small envelopes are better for some specimens, especially butterflies, moths, and other insects whose wings should be protected.

Carrying Equipment

A shallow, compartmentalized, shoulder hung, cloth bag should contain most items carried into the field. However, such things as a hand lens and forceps are best supported on strings hung around the neck. Also, equipment such as an insect net is best carried by hand.

Terrestrial Collecting

Invertebrates can be found in numbers in almost any terrestrial situation, at any time of the day or night, from early spring to late fall, in most places in the world. However, collecting normally is best in late spring or summer, during periods of warm, clear weather. Also, more animals are found when more habitats are examined.

Many different approaches are possible for a discussion of finding organisms. Here, the means is method of collecting.

Searching

In searching, only forceps, a moist brush, an aspirator, the fingers, or a killing jar are used to obtain invertebrates, and one relies upon the senses and a knowledge of nature to find animals.

Close examination of many sites in nature has the advantage of disclosing the precise habitat of individual animals. The main disadvantage is that fewer specimens are obtained than with other methods.

Searches usually are conducted on open ground, under objects on the ground, on and in plants, and under and among debris. To obtain specimens from plants, observe plant surfaces, especially among dense vegetative parts matted together by animals, and examine woody plants under the bark and in cracks and crevices. Also, use a pocket knife or scalpel to seek specimens within stems, leaves, roots, and galls; a hunting knife to peel bark; or a hand axe to split wood.

Best collecting from ground, nest, or other debris often requires some equipment. Even hand searching is improved if material first is spread on a white cloth or paper, or in a white tray. Even more productive is putting the debris through a 1/4-inch mesh *sieve* or *sifter*.

However, perhaps the best method uses a *Berlese type funnel*. This device is relatively easy to construct. A heat source, electric light or sun, is used to dry the debris placed into a funnel. Drying drives invertebrates down into a jar containing 80% alcohol or 5% formalin. The heat source should be neither too warm nor too cool; heat should dry the debris in three to five days.

Collecting from matted debris and vegetation or soil can prove difficult when only the above methods are applied. In such cases *flotation* might be useful. To obtain specimens, debris or soil is broken up, placed in a basin containing water, and the mixture stirred. Stirring helps float animals to the surface of the water. The process normally is more successful if magnesium sulfate is added. This chemical, a relaxant, anesthetizes the animals, thereby preventing their staying underwater.

Another aid to searching is *inundating*, a method using water to float or drive animals from their retreats. For example, in the field one may push plants underwater, pour water on soil (especially in aquatic environments), or add water and stir mud. Any of these techniques provides animals that can be picked up with forceps, an aspirator, the hands, etc.

A type of searching frequently ignored is *night collecting*. Collections just after sunset, during the night, and just prior to dawn often produce specimens difficult to encounter otherwise.

Such collections do not really involve a difference in technique unless one considers the use of flashlights, lanterns or head lamps to be sufficient modification to constitute new methodology.

Netting

Most people are familiar with the nets that are especially useful for collecting insects, but these nets can be used to capture other forms as well. A *general purpose net* should have a strong, light handle formed from about two to three feet of a 3/4-inch dowel or an old broom handle. Although the net's ring can be made by bending and attaching a wire coat hanger, a detachable 1/8-inch gauge, iron or steel ring that is 10 to 15 inches in diameter might be preferred. If the ring is detachable, damaged bags can be replaced in the field, and one can make and take afield bags for special purposes.

A general purpose netting bag, because it requires depth for aerial use, is 24 to 30 inches deep. The bag is of nylon netting and its edge is reinforced by heavy duty cloth forming a one-inch tube to receive the ring. Such a tube affords ease in replacement and resists wear.

If a net is made specifically for *aerial netting*, the bag may be of cotton, cheesecloth, or nylon netting. The bag should be light for ease in use, strong to resist wear, and netted to be seen through.

Capturing aerial invertebrates, usually insects, with a net is accomplished by sweeping the net through the air and, as part of a continuous motion, flipping the bag closed by placing the bottom of it into the open mouth of the ring.

Animals can be removed from nets in many ways. A common practice is to trap the animal in a fold of the bag with one hand, and then, with the other hand, insert a killing jar into the net and enclose the trapped invertebrate. Finally, the hand that trapped the invertebrate is shifted to close the top of the jar and the jar is withdrawn and corked or lidded. Very active animals and stinging or biting insects should be treated differently. After such invertebrates have been trapped in a bag fold, the fold is placed into a killing jar, and the jar is closed. When quiet, the animals can be removed from the net and placed into the jar.

A much different netting technique, *sweeping*, provides for the capture of a greater variety of invertebrates than does aerial netting. Owing to the strain sweeping places upon nets, a different type might be constructed. The handle can be as short as 18 inches and the ring as narrow as 8 inches in diameter. Also the bag might be of heavy duty muslin and be only 18 to 24 inches deep. All of these specifications produce nets that are both stronger and easier to use.

Sweeping involves rapid side strokes, in the form of continuous figure-8's, on herbs or woody plant foliage. The two primary precautions for this method are to avoid slow sweeps, which tend to lose invertebrates, and moist vegetation, which damages both invertebrates and nets.

Removal of invertebrates from a net should be frequent to avoid losing or damaging specimens. Taking animals by the direct application of a killing jar is difficult because of the debris collected during sweeping. Although a hand, forceps, brush, or aspirator can be used to select desired specimens, a two-step procedure is best. First, flying insects are extracted by using a *separator*. A separator is a light-tight box having both a lidded opening on top through which sweepings can be placed directly into the box and a single opening on the side, with a screw-top lid, which holds a killing jar. If sweepings are placed into the separator, flying insects will be attracted to the light admitted by the killing jar, and will enter the jar. Finally, when flying insects are subdued, the rest of the sweepings can be examined by hand or subjected to flotation (see "Searching").

Sugaring

Night-flying insects, especially moths, and certain other invertebrates are attracted to "sugar." "Sugar" is a mixture of such things as brown sugar, molasses, overripe fruit, stale beer, and/or rum. The mixture is "aged" a day or more until it ferments. Then, "sugar" is painted on upright objects, such as tree trunks and posts, along a "line"

of these objects. Invertebrates that feed upon the fermented material become sluggish; however, the collector must periodically visit the baited areas during the night. The invertebrates are not killed by the mixture, and one must be present to net, hand pick, aspirate, etc., them if collecting is to be effective.

Trapping

Of the many techniques that are effective in capturing invertebrates in various land habitats, we shall consider three: ground, ground emergence, and aerial trapping.

Ground traps can be constructed by burying a large juice can or jar to the lip, adding a waxed paper funnel to the lip, and placing a slightly raised wood or stone cover over the trap. Such a trap is best if baited. Meat, fermenting sap, decaying plant matter (especially fruit), and fresh or decaying fungi attract invertebrates. In a given habitat, the use of many differently baited traps, including unbaited traps, is most successful. Captured animals usually are easy to remove with an aspirator or to transfer into a killing jar.

Ground emergence traps obtain adult invertebrates as they emerge from the ground. Such traps are especially useful for insects. The trap is a pyramidal or conical, bottomless cage of screen, cheesecloth, or similar material. If placed in areas inhabited by developing animals about to emerge as adults, traps can be productive. Captured animals are either picked up with the fingers or aspirated prior to being placed in a killing jar, preservative, or bag for future transfer to a cage.

Aerial traps are cylindrical screen containers that are closed at one end and fitted with a funnel at the other end. Such traps are placed in suitable sites with their funnel ends closest to, but elevated from, the ground. Bait placed under the funnel opening will draw flying insects. The insects normally fly up through the funnel and into the trap when they leave the bait.

Beating

As the name of this technique implies, a heavy stick is used to strike shrub or tree branches. If two or three sharp, downward blows are made upon sturdy parts of woody plants, invertebrates are knocked almost straight down from their roost. However, dislodged animals are easier to find if they fall upon a white groundcover of cloth or paper.

Some collectors prefer to knock invertebrates onto a white or light-colored umbrella or a constructed beating sheet. The umbrella or beating sheet has the advantage of being hand held; animals are more likely to be caught by a receptacle that is close to the area being beaten.

A beating cloth can be made from about 2 by 3 feet of white, heavy cloth or canvas that is held open by crossed sticks. The sticks are tied, or better, screwed together. Each of the corners of the cloth should have a pocket to receive the ends of the crossed sticks.

A word of caution: It is not necessary to destroy or even damage plants severely. Sharp blows designed to jar animals loose need not do more than bruise bark. Most beaten plants will display no visible evidence of harm, especially if the amount of beating upon individuals is limited.

Shooting

The larger, stronger bodied, and elusive invertebrates might be shot, A particular type of load, called dust shot, causes a .22 calibre firearm to simulate a shotgun and does surprisingly little damage to specimens if not used too close to them. Generally, 15 feet is good range, but distance should be determined for the particular gun being used.

Freshwater Collecting

As is the case with terrestrial and marine collecting, invertebrates can be found in many freshwater habitats. Also, working at different times of the day and different seasons of the year increases the take. Moreover, the time of the year best for freshwater collecting roughly corresponds to the period best for terrestrial collecting.

Again, collecting techniques must be varied if the greatest success is desired. Since capturing, removing, emprisoning, and killing techniques have already been examined, discussion of them here is minimal.

Searching

Although generally favorable in all fresh water, the seeking of organisms in their exact site of occurrence is most successful in quiet waters, where animals are more abundant and less difficult to capture. Often, the hands, a small dip net, or forceps are satisfactory for capturing invertebrates. However, in hand picking one must beware of animals that bite; many, especially insects, can deliver painful bites.

Searching should be thorough. The exposed and under surfaces of stones should be examined, along with the surfaces and interior portions of sunken logs, tangled vegetation, and debris. In the case of debris, it is often worthwhile to remove the material and let it dry in the sun. As the debris dries, animals tend to move out of it; also, the drier the debris the easier it usually becomes to search by hand.

Netting and Screening

Nets and screens normally satisfy identical needs and both generally work best in moving water. *Aquatic nets* should be stronger than land nets. The handle should be sturdy and its length 2 to 6 feet, depending upon the way the net is to be used. The ring should be of 1/4-inch gauge iron or steel and about 8 inches in diameter, the narrowness providing added strength and ease of movement in narrow places. The ring may be round but should be triangular to broadly rounded. This flattening of the ring becomes an advantage when the net is placed upon the bottom of streams. Aquatic net bags can be of heavy nylon netting with the mesh determined by the minimum size of the animals desired but should be about 8 to 12 inches deep. A shallow bag is easier to handle and, owing to aquatic animal behavior, does not tend to lose specimens.

Although a special aquatic net is helpful, an aerial or general purpose terrestrial net may prove sufficient if its bag is of nylon netting. A nylon bag both dries quickly and is sturdy, advantageous features for a net used in water.

Screens can be constructed by attaching any convenient size of window screen to two stakes. This device often is preferred because when the stakes are driven into the bottom of the stream, the screen need not be tended.

Stream collecting is relatively easy if a net or screen is placed upon the stream bottom and across the flow of water. This should trap most or all of the water flow. After placement of the device, animals are disturbed upstream from the net or screen. This is accomplished by overturning rocks and wiping them by hand and by agitating bottom debris, mud, and/or sand with a stick. When animals are driven from their sites of concealment, water movement carries them to the collecting device.

Nets and screens also are useful in quiet water, where they can be manipulated by hand to collect animals observed on or near the surface.

Square or Apron Netting

Conventional aquatic nets may become entangled in dense aquatic vegetation or debris. In such situations a small square net or a spoon-shaped apron net is often used. The dimensions of these nets can vary; however, the smaller they are the easier they work. Owing to the rugged use to which they are put, they should be covered with wire screen.

Scraping

Although dredges are normally best for bottom collecting, a scraper is productive and much easier to construct. A scraper, or scraper net, is a square or rectangular box frame covered with wire screen and having a metal scraper on the lip. A strong handle supplies the durability and strength for sampling bottoms of shallow lakes and streams. Bottom materials can be brought to the water surface and the net shook so that the water removes fine material. Proper shaking leaves only specimens and larger debris to be examined.

Plankton Netting

A plankton net consists of mesh cloth formed into a funnel bag the large opening of which is supported by a 1/4-inch gauge steel ring, the narrow opening being shaped to receive a collecting bottle or vial. The net is moved through open water. If one ties drag lines to the steel ring, the plankton net can be either cast from shore and pulled toward land, or towed behind a boat. Naturally, the size of the mesh determines the minimum size of invertebrates and, unfortunately, debris collected.

Marine Collecting

Many of the terrestrial collecting techniques are suitable for exposed intertidal areas and many of the freshwater collecting techniques for shallow marine areas. However, special consideration of exposed rocky tidepools and mudflats is worthwhile.

Rocky Tidepools

Collecting usually is most profitable during a low tide, the lower the better. To select a good, low tide, one should obtain a local tide table—usually they are available at sporting goods stores. Newspapers originating from cities near the ocean frequently publish the time and depth of tides for a day or so in advance; however, such short notice may be insufficient.

Collecting rocky tidepool organisms can be very dangerous. One should follow the tide out and come back in with the tide. In rocky areas covered with seaweed there is a great chance of falling, but sneakers or tennis shoes and care minimize this hazard. Also, waves can and do wash the unwary off rocks. If awareness of danger comes too late to escape to high ground, lie down and hug the rocks or grasp seaweeds. Be assured, if one grasps the substrate, there is relatively little danger from being covered by water. However, a running person who is struck by a wave may be washed from shore.

Collecting equipment need not be elaborate. Forceps or tweezers, canvas or plastic bag or bucket, and plastic vials are excellent for gathering and bringing back specimens. A putty knife is of great help in obtaining gastropods and chitons and of even more use in lifting fragile specimens, e.g., ribbonworms, from the substrate. A geologist's pick, hammer and chisel, and/or crowbar are needed if rocks are to be broken. A hand lens is helpful to examine small specimens, and a notebook and pencil or pen to collect data.

Plan your collecting:

1. Work along the water's edge but be aware of ocean waves.

2. Examine all surfaces and holes in rocks. Look in cracks and under ledges of large rocks. Break up *some* soft rock.

3. Examine upon and within dense masses of animals and algae, especially among the rootlike algae holdfasts.

4. Examine the above habitats in deep, shaded pools, especially those farther out.

5. Examine gravel, sand, and mud that appears not to have been churned recently by the ocean. Running such material through a seive is productive.

6. Avoid taking more than one or two of the same thing. If others are collecting, let them obtain their own specimens. Most likely you will not find more than one or two examples of organisms they do not find.

7. Do not keep, or perhaps even disturb, more than you can examine, display, and/or preserve.

8. Do not put carnivorous or active animals in a container with forms they will destroy.

9. If possible, keep collected organisms healthy by changing their water when your field trip takes a long time.

Mudflats

Mud and sandy mud, exposed in bays and like surroundings, are frequently subject to surface examination and to digging. Mud can be shoveled into a screen box, the box agitated in water, and specimens extracted from the residue. However, "the mud flat stomp," (named by my students) is the most useful, simple method.

The stomp is performed by a group of people stomping the mud until it becomes semiliquid and animals float to the surface. This procedure supplies many so-called rare animals. For example, 23 innkeepers were floated up from a site about 12 feet in diameter. Although the method does seem destructive, the same small area has been equally productive over the last seven years. In fact, the greatest number of innkeepers were taken from the site on the sixth year of stomping.

In our experience, one must liquify both a surface and a separate subsurface layer of harder mud before animals are found in significant numbers. This requires some effort on the part of stompers. Also, owing to fatigue, collectors may sink into the mud. However, if they keep moving at all times while in the mud, this possibility is minimized.

Another technique is especially useful to obtain small, frequently overlooked animals. All that is required is a bucket, bicycle or like pump, and a sheet of white paper. To collect animals, a layer of mud is placed in a bucket of sea water and the pump is used to mix the mud and water thoroughly. Then, the sheet of paper is placed flat upon the surface of the mixture. The small animals will become trapped upon the surface film of the mixture and soon will adhere to the paper.

REARING

Keeping animals alive in captivity can be fascinating. One may rear invertebrates merely as a hobby, perhaps solely for the purpose of photography, or as a means of obtaining certain scientific information. If one clearly has no scientific interest in invertebrates but still wishes to do more than observe them in nature, rearing is recommended.

Rearing may be complete or partial. Complete rearing is caring for animals during all stages of their life cycles and, naturally, is more difficult than handling them only at specific stages.

Successful rearing, complete or partial, requires familiarity with the life cycle or stage involved. One must know the habits and exact habitat, including its physical environment, of each stage being kept in captivity. Especially important are feeding habits and the temperature and moisture conditions of the natural environments. In other words, one must really know the natural history of animals being caged.

Although rearing often is difficult and leads to frequent failure, certain considerations increase the possibility of success. Cage size is generally less important than one might expect. Rarely can unsuccessful rearing be traced to cage size alone. Therefore, if one is especially careful to note food, temperature, moisture, and habitat in nature and attempt to duplicate them, efforts may be successful. Very important in such considerations is how invertebrates obtain water. Some obtain water strictly from their food, others from dew on plants or the substrate, and others from standing water. Often the natural source of water must be simulated.

PHOTOGRAPHING

Photographing invertebrates and all other things of nature takes many forms. For example, invertebrate photography may involve dead, anesthetized, chilled, caged, or wild subjects. Although all such work generally is called nature photography, obviously only shots of unrestricted animals and objects in their habitat satisfies this designation. The various kinds of invertebrate photography are generally related to the photographer's purpose in studying nature. The efforts of a photographer, might lead to creative photography if he is not interested in learning or presenting nature as it is. (There is no reason why anyone should be boorish enough to belittle or otherwise criticize such efforts.) Another photographer may have little interest in other aspects of working in nature but can provide excellent examples of candid photography in the wild. However, the overall nature enthusiast, if a photographer, should concentrate, at least in part, on nature as it is.

Nature photography requires special equipment and technical skill, subjects well covered in the selected references. In addition, one's success is related directly to his knowledge of nature. Obviously, the more one knows about the natural history of a particular animal the more he will know about where and when to find it and how it will behave. However, the neophyte should not dismiss

nature photography from consideration, because it frequently is an aid to learning.

COLLECTIONS

This is one of the more ambitious goals for those studying invertebrates. Collections are extremely time consuming because they necessitate handling, preserving, labeling, and storing specimens. Storage includes the never-ending chore of maintenance. All of these considerations become major points in the following discussion.

Specimen Handling

Further handling of animals is usually necessary during the processes of preservation. Handling is critical because one must keep specimens tagged so data are not lost. To keep animals tagged, it is best to work with one collection number at a time. All animals bearing one number can be preserved and placed into a single container until the labeling process is completed. This container may be a jar or tray, if specimens are preserved in liquid, or a box, if specimens are dried. If there are insects whose wings are to be spread, individual spreading boards should be limited to animals bearing the same collection number.

These procedures may have to be modified so that one can keep collection numbers on each specimen, up to and through the process of labeling. However, once labeling is completed, the task of always linking specimens with their data is ended, and the collection can be stored.

Preservation Techniques

The preservation techniques and chemicals applied to specimens can vary, even for members of the same stage in the life cycle of a single species. However, our discussion will be generalized, and only techniques satisfactory for most purposes will be examined. We will consider anesthetics and preservatives, the latter in reference to fixation and storage of specimens.

Although techniques can be generalized for most animals, insects require special procedures. For this reason discussion is further separated into two topics, most invertebrates and insects.

Most Invertebrates

Animals can be collected by means other than the field killing methods already given. In fact, many aquatic and parasitic, and some terrestrial animals maintain their form and make good specimens only if relaxed, or anesthetized prior to fixation. Numerous zoological specimens are hardly recognizable because the time-consuming process of relaxation was omitted. However, anesthesia is often applied to the point of killing. In addition, there is no simple rule to determine whether or not a particular specimen should or should not be relaxed.

Frequently, anesthetics and preservatives are identical. Both will be considered prior to a discussion of actual techniques at the phylum level.

Anesthetics

There are many anesthetics, some liquid, others solid, but no single one is best for all forms. Perhaps the best all-around anesthetic for aquatic life is a magnesium chloride solution (73.2 g/liter distilled water) mixed 1:1 with water of an animal's environment. Other widely used materials also are liquid. Stock formalin (40%) or stock alcohol (95 or 100%) is added drop-by-drop to liquid covering the specimen. Of the alcohols, ethyl or a mixture called reagent is best, isopropyl second choice, and wood, or methyl, least desirable. Another, and very simple, liquid technique is slowly heating the water containing the specimen. Also, one can place animals in boiled water.

Certain solid anesthetics are convenient because they are added gradually to make a concentrated solution. Useful chemicals of this sort include methol sulfate, magnesium sulfate, and chlorotone.

No matter what anesthetic is used, it should be added slowly to a container having a minimum of water (and, of course, the animal).

Preservatives

As with relaxants, there is no single preservative that is best for all animals. However, two liquids satisfy most needs. Alcohol (70% reagent, ethyl, or isopropyl) has the disadvantage of not hardening some soft parts, but otherwise is preferable to formalin. Formalin (one part of stock formalin to ten parts water, sea water for marine animals) may harden animals too much and corrode some structures. The corrosion defect can be remedied in most cases by neutralization of this acid, e.g., with calcium carbonate. Also, a general problem, lack of flexibility, can be solved by adding glycerine (to 5% of the preservative with most forms, 20% with arthropods).

Note: When used on soft-bodied animals, preservatives should be added slowly, perhaps drop-by-drop, to preserve body form. Also, any percentage of formalin mentioned is of the stock solution, as purchased, generally a 40% solution of formaldehyde. Finally, it is recommended that the collector use a tray, partly filled with wax or, better, commercially prepared material, which allows specimens to be arranged and pinned in desired positions prior to being fixed with liquid.

Porifera

Anesthetic—none.
Fixation—95% alcohol or 10% neutralized formalin.
Store—70–90% alcohol or 3–5% neutralized formalin.

Spicules—boil in 5% potassium hydroxide or clorox—wash —centrifuge—95% alcohol—put on slide—xylene wash—piccolyte—cover slip.

Coelenterata and Ctenophora

Anesthetic—menthol or magnesium chloride (long process; make frequent changes of anesthetic); also deep freeze sea anemones to block in sea water.
Fix—10% formalin, should neutralize for corals and comb jellies; frozen block should thaw in somewhat stronger fix.
Store—3–5% formalin or 70% alcohol.

Add fix and store solutions very slowly; use drop method if possible.

Platyhelminthes

Anesthetic—heat slowly in water.
Fix—10% formalin.
Store—5% formalin.

Special techniques are required for microscope slide preparation.

Nemertea

Anesthetic—magnesium chloride until no reaction; keep isolated; very difficult to prevent from breaking.
Fix—10% neutral formalin or 95% alcohol.
Store—80% alcohol.

Acanthodephala and Aschelminthes (macroscopic forms)

Anesthetic—gradually heat in water or use magnesium chloride; be sure Acanthocephala snouts are out.
Fix—10% formalin (Acanthocephala snout may have to be held out with forceps).
Store—5% formalin or 70% alcohol.

Entoprocta and Ectoprocta

Anesthetic—menthol or magnesium chloride; check under microscope until tentacles cannot be stimulated to contract.
Fix—5% neutral formalin.
Store—5% neutral formalin or wash and 30–50–70% alcohol.

Phoronida (see Annelida)

Brachiopoda

Follow the procedure given for Entoprocta and Ectoprocta, but add a wood chip between the valves when organism relaxes. Also, to make a dry specimen of the hard parts, start with a preserved specimen in 70% alcohol and treat it as follows:
50% alcohol (24 hours)—30% alcohol (24 hours)—water— add potassium hydroxide until concentrated—keep hot (do

not boil) until soft parts dissolve—cool-wash in water—let dry.

Sipunculoidea (see Annelida)

Mollusca

May remove soft parts and save shell.

Soft-bodied forms without shells—see Coelenterata and Cnidaria.

Chitons (remove soft parts or):

Collect—wrap flat on sticks to prevent their curling.

Kill—place chitons on sticks into 160°F water.

Store—70% alcohol or 3–5% neutral formalin.

Shelled forms in liquid:

Anesthetic—magnesium chloride or warm in water; put wood chip between clam valves; many large gastropods die fully expanded if placed in closed jar containing sea water but no air space.

Fix—5% neutral formalin or 70% alcohol.

Store—3–5% neutral formalin or 70% alcohol.

Echiuroidea

Kill—Gradually warm water; do not take water above 150°F.

Fix—5% formalin.

Store—5% formalin.

Annelida

Anesthetic—magnesium chloride or gradually warm in water kept below 150° F; many marine forms have a snout which might have to be forced out with forceps.

Fix—snout, if present, might have to be held out with forceps; 10% formalin, often better if injected (do not distend abnormally).

Store—3–5% formalin; alcohol leaves body soft and flabby but can be used after hardening with formalin.

Echiuroidea (see Annelida, generally no proboscis problem)

Arthropoda

Minute and microscopic forms should be prepared on slides.

Wormlike forms are prepared like Annelida.

Land forms:

Kill—insect killing jar or 70% alcohol.

Fix—unneutralized formalin weakens and destroys external skeletons; 70% alcohol or better, 20% glycerine (for joint flexibility) in 70% alcohol; make slits in body for fixative penetration.

Store—in fixing agent or dry.

Aquatic forms:

Kill—magnesium chloride anesthetic works well for many forms but many others will drop their legs; procedures that may work are fresh water for ma-

rine forms, desiccation, gradually warming water to just below 150°, and gradually adding (drop method) formalin to 5% and alcohol to 70%.

Fix and Store—see Arthropod land forms.

Echinodermata

Most—simply drop into or inject with a 10% formalin solution; leave in solution one day; and take out and let dry.

Others:

Anesthetic—magnesium chloride; long for sea cucumbers: to stop tentacle retraction when stimulated with forceps; starfish upside down so tube feet extend easily; sea urchins, small hole to let in preservative.

Fix—sea cucumbers, few minutes into 5% formalin while holding tentacles with forceps, 70% alcohol into cloaca and body cavity with hypo; rest 70% alcohol.

Store—70% alcohol.

Best sea urchin technique—dip in paraffin—inject 95% alcohol into body—lay aside 24 hours—remove paraffin by dipping into xylene—store dry or in 70% alcohol.

Chaetognatha and Hemichordata (like Entoprocta and Ectoprocta but no tentacle problem)

Pogonophora (not likely to be found; like Entoprocta and Ectoprocta)

Chordata

Lancets (like Entoprocta and Ectoprocta but no tentacle problem)

Tunicates:

Anesthetic—1 heaping teaspoon magnesium sulfate to liter of sea water; leave 12–24 hours.

Fix—1 hour in 10% formalin or 70% alcohol.

Store—5% formalin.

Insects

Insects are preserved in various ways. Although for certain uses many require involved preservation methods, none of these special techniques will be considered here. For most purposes, it is satisfactory to either place an insect in a vial of preservative or dry mount it on a pin or point.

Vials

Soft-bodied and minute animals are placed in small vials containing alcohol or formalin solutions. Although an 80% reagent or ethyl alcohol solution generally is preferred, a 5% formalin solution is easier to maintain, cheaper, and less difficult to acquire. The following orders or parts of orders of insects are placed in vials:

Protura

Thysanura

MOUNTING INSECTS

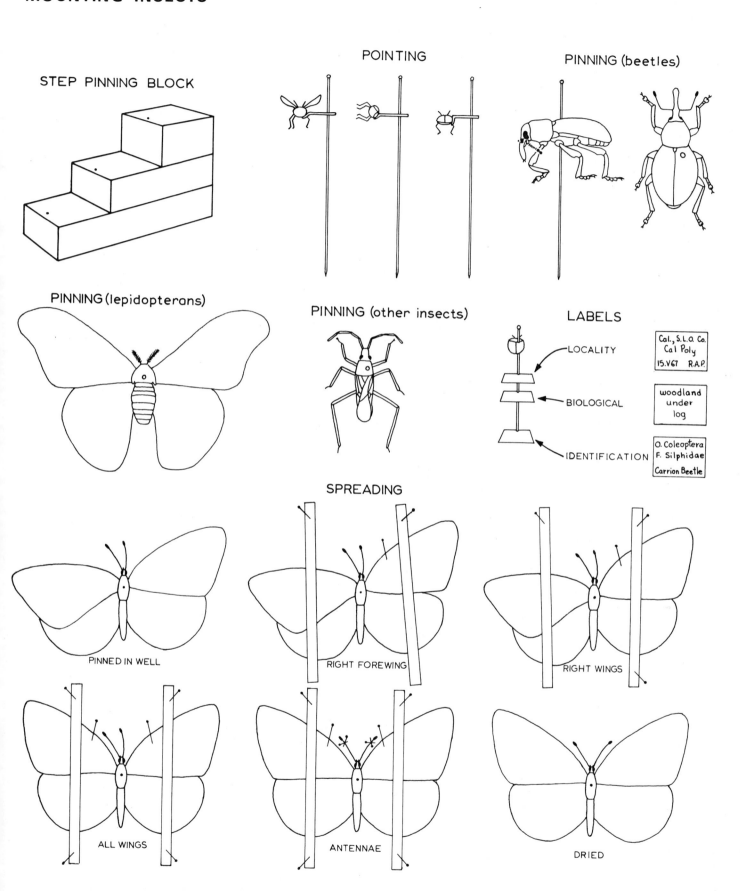

STEP PINNING BLOCK

POINTING

PINNING (beetles)

PINNING (lepidopterans)

PINNING (other insects)

LABELS

LOCALITY

Cal., S.L.O. Co.
Cal Poly
15.V.67   R.A.P.

BIOLOGICAL

woodland
under
log

IDENTIFICATION

O. Coleoptera
F. Silphidae
Carrion Beetle

SPREADING

PINNED IN WELL

RIGHT FOREWING

RIGHT WINGS

ALL WINGS

ANTENNAE

DRIED

Collembola
Emphemeroptera
Isoptera
Plecoptera
Dermaptera
Psocoptera
Zoraptera
Mallophaga
Anopleura
Thysanoptera
Homoptera—plant lice and perhaps whiteflies, scale insects and mealybugs.
Strepsiptera
Trichoptera
Siphonaptera
Minute forms of any order.

Mounting

Mounting is done in one of two ways, pinning or pointing; however, pinning may also require spreading of the wings. Both methods involve the use of insect pins, which are made in many sizes, generally 000 to 7. Usually the following sizes will suffice: 1 for ladybug size, 2 for honeybee size, and 3 for larger insects.

The actual processes of mounting will be discussed as three topics, pinning, pointing, and spreading. However, certain related important items bear consideration. These are relaxing, eviscerating, degreasing, and step pinning blocks.

Relaxing

Do not confuse moistening (relaxing) dry insects with anesthetizing (also relaxing) live invertebrates.

If, prior to mounting, insects are allowed to become too dry, difficulties arise. Although insects can be made pliable if placed in a jar containing damp sand, such relaxing should be avoided. Often moistening is either excessive or deficient for ease in mounting, especially if wing spreading is required. The wise collector will do his best to avoid having to relax specimens.

Eviscerating

Certain groups, especially Orthoptera, have abundant abdominal fats. If the fats are not removed, the process of decay destroys the specimens.

Removal of abdominal materials requires first, slitting the abdomen on the underside and then, scooping out the contents. In some, but not most, cases it is necessary to stuff the abdomen with cotton to prevent deformation during drying.

Degreasing

Many mounted specimens, especially beetles, eventually will release fats from their bodies. This release usually is not related to overall decay, but it does cause specimens to become dust collectors, sometimes so much so as to obscure body parts. However, this can be prevented if, prior to mounting, greasy insects are put through changes in ethyl ether until the final liquid does not yellow.

Step Pinning Blocks

Pinning and pointing are simplified if a step pinning block is used to place insects, points, and data tags at various levels on a single pin. This device looks like a staircase that has small holes near the front of each "step." The holes, just large enough to receive an insect pin easily, are 3/8, 5/8, and 1 inch deep, as one "goes up the stairs." These blocks can be purchased or made from a fairly durable material like wood; however, it is cheapest and easiest to make them from cardboard glued together.

Pinning

Insects, except Coleoptera and Lepidoptera, are pinned just to the right of the center of the thorax, the Coleoptera through the right elytron (hard forewing) near the front center, and the Lepidoptera through the center of the thorax.

The pin is placed so both the front-to-rear and the side-to-side axes of the animal are perpendicular to the shaft of the pin. Then, the point of the pin is placed in the 1-inch deep hole of the step pinning block and the insect run up the pin until the pin point reaches the 1-inch depth barrier.

As was stated previously, not all insects are mounted. However, there are not always strict rules as to whether a specimen is to be pinned or pointed. One way of avoiding indecision is to use the ladybug as a dividing point, pinning all animals of equal size or larger and pointing all smaller ones.

All except the minute forms of the following orders or parts of orders are pinned or pointed:
Odonata—dragonfly wings may be spread and damselfly wings supported in a natural position, together and above the body.
Orthoptera—at least the right pair of wings are spread in winged forms.
Hemiptera
Homoptera—cicadas and hoppers; others generally in vials; scale insects may be dried and mounted on their host plants.
Neuroptera—large forms may have the wings spread.
Coleoptera
Mecoptera
Lepidoptera—wings must be spread.
Diptera—large forms may have the wings spread.
Hymenoptera

SPREADING BOARD

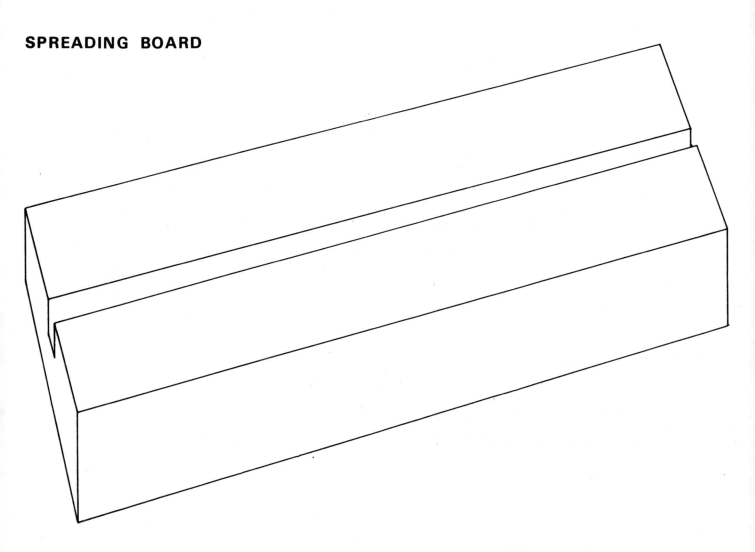

Pointing

Points are triangular pieces of light cardboard or celluloid, about 8 to 10 mm. long, and 3 to 4 mm. wide at the base. They can be cut out with scissors or a point punch.

Mounting on points is fairly simple. First, a pin should be placed through the center of the point 3 to 4 mm. from the base of the point. Second, the tip of the upper side of the point is touched to glue. Finally, the glued tip is stuck to the insect.

Pointed specimens have either their sides or their backs up. If the wings extend above the body, as is the case in flies and wasps, mounting is on the side to protect the wings. For specimens with the back pointed upward, the underparts must not be completely hidden, because identification might require their being examined. For this reason, beetles frequently are glued by their right side to the tip of a point that is bent 90° downward. The point tip is also bent downward slightly for other insects. In all cases, when examined, point tips are directed to the left and the insects' abdomens are closest to the observer.

The positions of legs and wings usually are not considered too important. However, it is best to use some care and have these structures dry in a more-or-less lifelike position.

Spreading

The position of the wings is considered most important in two groups, Lepidoptera and Orthoptera. In Lepidoptera both pairs and in Orthoptera at least the right wings are spread. In both cases, wings are placed so the leading edge of the hind wing and trailing edge of the forewing are perpendicular, or essentially so, to the insect's body. One or both pairs of wings may be aligned in a similar manner to the previously indicated large-winged insects.

Materials necessary for spreading include insect pins, narrow (about 1/8 inch wide) strips of paper, and a spreading board. A spreading board is a rectangular block about 6 1/4 by 12 by 1 1/2 inches having a well about 1/4 inch wide and 1/2 inch deep—the well bisects the 6 1/4 inches width and runs the 12 inches or more of length. Because spread insects should be left about a week on a board, many boards might be needed. Boards can be assembled from the following materials:

1. Two 1/2-inch high stacks of corrugated cardboard pieces, each piece about 3 by 12 inches, but all the same dimensions.

2. About 1-inch thick fiberboard that is 6 1/2 inches wide by 12 inches long. A stack of corrugated cardboard of the same dimensions will substitute.

3. Individual pieces for each 1/2-inch stack of 3 by 12 inches corrugated cardboard are glued together with plastic glue to provide two pieces of layered, corrugated cardboard, each 3 by 12 by 1/2 inches.

4. The two pieces formed in step 3 are glued to the fiberboard (or substituted glued stack of corrugated cardboard) leaving a well in the center and along the length of the 12-inch dimension.

If many spreading boards are made, the width of the wells should be varied somewhat; 3/8-inch wells will accomodate broader bodied and 3/16-inch wells narrower bodied animals with greater ease.

Spreading a butterfly or moth is accomplished as follows:

1. The insect pin, containing the lepidopteran to be spread, is pushed into the bottom of the spreading board well, until the bases of the wings are level with the top of the well. If the butterfly or moth is not at the proper final height on the pin, later attempts to raise it usually will destroy the specimen.

2. Paper strips, extending about one inch beyond the front and rear of the body, are pinned at the front end at a convenient distance from the spreading board well.

3. The right side of the body is immobilized by placing pins, close to the body.

4. The free end of the right-hand paper strip is held loosely over the right wing while the point of the pin is inserted through the forewing at a place behind the strong front margin vein and near the base of the wing. Then, the forewing is moved forward until its rear margin is perpendicular to the body. This position is secured by pushing the point of the pin slightly into the spreading board.

5. According to a procedure similar to step 4, the hindwing is pulled forward so the forewing slightly overlaps the hindwing.

6. The paper strip is pulled tightly and the free, rear end is pinned to the spreading board.

7. Steps 2 through 6 are repeated for the left wings.

8. Pins are used to arrange the antennae so that they are parallel to the front margins of the forewings.

9. To eliminate the possibility of wing curling, strips of glass or microscopic slides can be placed upon the wings.

The right wings of grasshoppers are spread by a similar technique whereby the front margin of the right hind wing is set perpendicular to the body, and the rear margin of the right fore wing just reaches the front margin of the hind wing. *Warning:* Specimens should be left on a spreading board for at least a week. In most climates average sized individuals will dry in three or four days; however, if the weather is damp or the bodies are large, two weeks or more may be necessary for drying. You can determine if a specimen is dry by probing the abdomen. If the abdomen can be moved independently of the wings, the animal must be left on the spreading board; if the specimen is stiff, it is dry and can be removed. Artificial heat may be used to hasten drying, but extreme care must be taken or the body will be damaged.

One must protect specimens during all stages of the preservation process. There are many insects, and even mice, that will consider your incipient collection a convenient free meal.

Labeling

The above steps provide properly preserved specimens. The next step is to write data in India ink on labels. Three items of data are written identification, locality, and biological information. These data are separated into three parts for each insect but are not separated for other invertebrates. For insects, the three labels are as follows:

1. The one for locality data includes three subdivisions, place of capture (state, county, and locale), date of capture, and collector (usually initials). The date may be abbreviated. May 15, 1967, is transposed to day, month, and year and written 15.V-67.

2. The one for biological data records, as a minimum, the collection number, the habitat of capture, e.g., digger pine-blue oak woodland, and the specific site of capture, e.g., under blue oak log.

3. The one for identification has the scientific and common name of the specimen—scientific names obtained from this book will never be more precise than family, but common names of species, if known, may be used.

Whether one or three tags are used, they are placed with the specimens. If an insect is in a jar or vial, usually the locality and biological labels are placed within the jar or vial, and the identification label is pinned next to the container. For any other invertebrate, a single, all-inclusive label is placed within or attached upon the container.

All insect tags are of the same size, 1/2 inch by 3/8 inch, and are placed on pins bearing pinned or pointed specimens. In their final arrangement, they are oriented to read from the rear of the insect. Each is pinned through its center top margin, in a definite order, and at a specific distance from the point of the pin:

First, the locality label is pinned and pushed up 5/8 inch from the tip of the pin point. Next, the biological data label is pinned and pushed up 3/8 inch from the tip of the pin point. Then, the identification label is pinned flush with the surface of the collection box. Finally, all pins are pushed about 1/8 inch into the bottom of the box. The various distances are easier to maintain if a step pinning block is used.

Collection Storage

Although some maintenance is required, commercially made boxes for dry specimens and museum jars for liquid specimens will store invertebrates in good condition for a lifetime or longer. However, cigar boxes and food jars, although strictly makeshift substitutes, often are satisfactory. Later, more will be said about the care of completed collections.

Collection Containers

If stored in museum jars, liquid specimens cause the least future problems. If food jars are used, lids might corrode. However, this tendency for corrosion is minimized if a waterproof, full gasket is seated inside the lid. Also spraying its inside with plastic and letting the plastic dry thoroughly before the lid is used to seal the jar often proves helpful.

Dry collections may be housed in cigar boxes, constructed boxes, or commerical boxes. If the containers are to be used for pinned insects, the bottoms are prepared by lining them with cork or fiberboard. Styrofoam might substitute here, but the chemical pesticides stored with dry invertebrates often destroy it. Therefore, if a styrofoam bottom is used, repellants are placed in an aluminum foil-lined container (a very small box will do) that is anchored in a corner of the box.

If boxes are used for other invertebrates, it may be advantageous to compartmentalize them. Divided boxes keep specimens and their labels together—labels can be attached to the wall of each unit. Also each compartment can be lined, at least on the bottom, with cotton, cloth, or other materials. Cotton has both the advantage and disadvantage of holding specimens within their containers.

Arrangement

Invertebrate collections are arranged taxonomically, as is the sequence of animals in this manual. To accomplish this, individual jars and, if practical, boxes should be devoted to a specific group of animals, the "kinds" of invertebrates recognized in this book. However, it is often impractical to place only one "kind" in a single box. If a box is used for more than one group, e.g., a family, the scope should be increased taxonomically, e.g., an order, class, or perhaps phylum. When individual boxes and jars are thus organized, the entire collection can be worked with ease.

Collection Care

Unfortunately, once a collection is assembled, the work is not completed. Because you have gone to some trouble to make a collection and because of its potential future value, you should do the things necessary to keep it in good condition. Moreover, if you are to let a collection deteriorate, there is no justification for the destruction of life that was involved.

Liquid collections are checked at least once, preferably more often, a year. One should be sure that the lids are still in excellent condition and that the preservative still covers the specimens. It is likely that some lids will need replacement, and many jars will require additional preservative.

Dry collections are subject to insect and other pest attack. To combat this, certain chemicals are of help. These repellents and pesticides are sometimes available at drugstores and always available from a biological supply house. The following materials generally are preferred.

Naphthalene flakes are most widely used because they volatize slowly, remain in solid form for several weeks, serve as an excellent repellent, and kill invertebrates if they are present.

Paradichlorobenzene voltilizes faster and is good for collections under attack, but does not protect for as long as naphthalene flakes.

It is recommended that one use a heaping tablespoon of naphthalene mixed with a heaping tablespoon of paradichlorobenzene in each collection box. This mixture should be applied a minimum of twice a year.

Certain chemicals are still better for collections under attack, but do not have much effect after three or four days of application. Among these chemicals are carbon disulfide and carbon tetrachloride. Carbon disulfide is dangerously inflammable; if ignited it may explode. However, carbon disulfide in combination with carbon tetrachloride loses its explosive power. Unfortunately, these two pesticides can be harmful to man. Carbon tetrachloride, especially, is a deadly poison.

Further protection against pests is afforded by sealing collection boxes. Also, painting cigar boxes, in addition to improving their appearance, often deters pests.

A final aspect of collection care involves the handling of dry specimens. When a collection becomes very dry, the specimens are very brittle and easily broken. Naturally, any mutilation will result in a specimen of less value.

SOME BIOLOGICAL SUPPLY HOUSES

Carolina Biological Supply Co., Burlington, North Carolina 27216.

General Biological Supply House, Inc., 8200 South Hoyne Ave., Chicago, Illinois 60620.

National Biological Supply Company, Inc., 2325 South Michigan Ave., Chicago, Illinois 60616.

Van Waters & Rogers, Inc., P. O. Box 3200, Rincon Annex, San Francisco, California 94119.

Ward's Natural Science Establishment, Inc., P. O. Box 1712, Rochester, New York 14603.

Ward's of California, P. O. Box 1749, Monterey, California 93942.

SELECTED REFERENCES

Bierne, B. P. 1955. Collecting, preparing and preserving insects. Canada Dept. of Agriculture, Entomology Division Publ. 932.

Borror, D. J., and D. M. Delong. 1964. An introduction to

the study of insects. rev. ed. Holt, Rinehart & Winston, Inc., New York.

Edmondson, W. T. (ed.) 1959. Ward and Whipple's fresh-water biology. 2nd Ed. John Wiley & Sons, Inc., New York.

Gray, P. 1954. The microtomist's formulary and guide. Blakiston, now McGraw-Hill Book Company, Inc., New York.

Gray, P. (ed.) 1961. The encyclopedia of biological sciences. Reinhold Publishing Corporation, New York.

Kinne, R. 1962. The complete book of nature photography. A. S. Barnes & Company, Inc., New York.

Linton, D. 1964. Photographing nature. Natural History Press, Garden City, New York.

Miller, D. F., and G. W. Blaydes. 1962. Methods and materials for teaching the biological sciences. 2nd Ed. McGraw-Hill Book Company, Inc., New York.

Needham, J. G., et al. 1937. Culture methods for invertebrate animals. Comstock Publishing Co., Ithaca, N. Y. 1959 reprint by Dover Publications, Inc., New York.

Pennak, R. W. 1959. Fresh-water invertebrates of the United States. The Ronald Press Co., New York.

Peterson, A. 1959. Entomological techniques. How to work with insects. Edwards Brothers, Inc., Ann Arbor, Michigan.

Ross, E. S. 1953. Insects close up. University of California Press, Berkeley.

Smith, R. I. (ed.) 1954. Intertidal invertebrates of the Central California Coast. University of California Press, Berkeley.

Wagstaffe, R., and J. H. Fidler. 1955. The preservation of natural history specimens. Vol. 1, invertebrates. Witherby, London.

IDENTIFYING INVERTEBRATES

Part II, North American Invertebrates, is organized on the basis of the assumption that the reader is completely unfamiliar with invertebrates. Since this is not always the case, the index provides the page numbers of sections dealing with animals the reader may already be familiar with, such as snails, crabs, and starfishes. Hence one can determine the kind of snail, crab, or starfish without following the procedure for a completely unknown animal.

"North American Invertebrates" contains 22 primary divisions, the 22 recognized phyla of animals. Many phyla are further subdivided on a taxonomic basis (explained in the foregoing discussion of biological classification). This means that for any entirely unknown animal the collector must make one of 22 choices, i.e., determine its phylum, then perhaps he will determine its class (subphylum in the case of arthropods), order and family or part of family.

Choices from phylum to family are aided in two ways, illustrations and diagnoses, which should be used interdependently. In addition to providing figures of animals, the illustrations may indicate size, important structures for identification, and sometimes distribution. Size may be given numerically or graphically. Graphically, lines provide a single average length or the range between minimum and maximum length. For some insects, size is related to wingspread, abbreviated WS. Key external structures in identification often are pointed out by a line or arrow.

Diagnoses include significant external structure, life cycle, habitat, feeding habits, and other behavior helpful in identification. Although technical terms are avoided, when needed, they are linked to illustrations.

Familiarity with organisms is the key to proficiency in identifying more living things. The more animals one knows, the easier it is to identify others, because one learns what is and what is not important. However, diagnostic criteria vary greatly among comparable groups. For example, diagnoses of subunits within insect orders vary considerably among the various orders. In other words, there appears to be no short cut. The types of diagnoses used here are necessary.

Unless a beginner is very fortunate, he will find animals he cannot identify. Such specimens should be taken or sent to a specialist at a nearby college, university, or museum. (It is illegal to send alive many kinds of animals by mail or other carriers.) Most specialists will help you with your difficulties if your specimens are in good condition and your requests are reasonable. However, if you expect or demand immediate help, you should not and probably will not receive it. Also, you should not seek identification of large amounts of material. Moreover, do not simply take or send material. Your first step should be to write or phone, describing the quantity, nature, and collecting data of the animals.

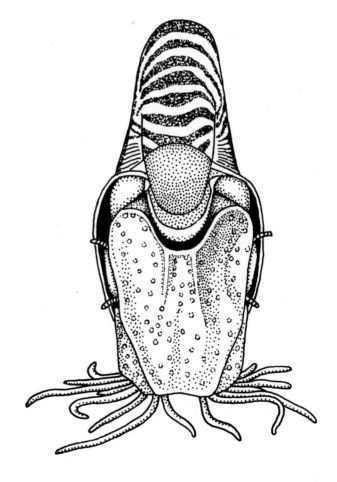

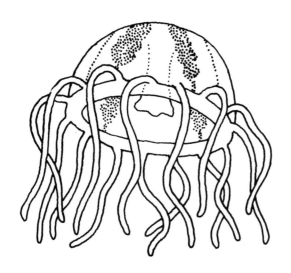

PART 2 NORTH AMERICAN INVERTEBRATES

MESOZOA (MESOZOANS)

Diagnosis: minute to about .4 inch long; body organization consists of an outer layer (either of cells or of nuclei not separated into individual cells) surrounding 1 or more reproductive cells; life cycle complicated, with an alternation of sexual and asexual generations.

Habitat: internal parasites; 2 orders, 1 parasitic in the kidneys of squids and octupi, the other in the internal spaces and tissues of various invertebrates (flatworms, ribbonworms, brittle stars, segmented worms, and clams).

PORIFERA (SPONGES)

Diagnosis: solitary or colonial as adults, occur as thin crusts, plantlike branches, and vaselike, globular or irregular masses; colors range from gray or drab to brilliant red, orange, yellow, blue, violet, or black; without mouth or organs of any kind; body permeated with pores, canals, and chambers through which a water current flows; body generally rigid and spiny or velvety to the touch, rarely slimy; adults sedentary but many capable of contracting body (minute or more) in response to touch or drying, openings often closed when exposed to air; growth by spreading and branching, plantlike; reproduction sexual, sexes separate and involving a larval stage, or asexual; asexual reproduction of 2 types, budding of individuals from parent colony and gemmule formation; gemmules consist of a group of cells surrounded by a protective wall, commoner in freshwater sponges; when ponds freeze or dry and adult sponges die, gemmules remain to start a new sponge as soon as favorable conditions return; amazing powers of regeneration, after adult has been put through a seive cells reunite regenerating many small sponges, adults filter feeders from water circulated by the sponge individual or colony through its body.

Sponges may be confused with Ectoprocta, Entoprocta, some Chordata (tunicates), and some algae. Sponges usually possess 1 or more visible openings that lead into a single or complex of cavities, depending upon their being solitary or colonial forms; the other phyla do not. Individuals in a sponge colony mass are not discernible but ectoprocts and entoprocts (though minute) are, and the confusing tunicates usually are. The confusing algae form smooth, rocklike, usually purple, crusts, or are irregularly shaped and green or greenish black. When torn open, only sponges display complex cavities.

Habitat: marine, intertidal to deep sea, except for one freshwater family; most adults are attached to rocks or organisms.

Class Calcarea (Calcispongiae) (Calcareous or Limy Sponges)

Diagnosis: typically solitary or colonial, vase-shaped organisms; some form bushy or compact masses, and a few have stalklike bases; spicules, or spines, of calcium carbonate (dissolve in acid) usually cause a bristly surface; mostly drab, inconspicuous animals less than 6 inches long; generally whitish to light grayish, also yellowish, brownish, dark brown, or bluish gray; strictly marine organisms occupying intertidal to 3000-foot waters, most likely found in tidepools either on rocks, or within cracks and crevices in rocks, or on seaweed holdfasts (rootlike structures); recognizable growth forms are vase, bristle, limy crust, and antler sponges.

Vase Sponges (Order Heterocoela)—body egglike to elongate, vaselike; body wall thickened and folded internally; solitary or colonial; intertidal types figured.
Bristle Sponges (Order Homocoela)—body globular to irregularly so; body wall thin and not folded internally.
Limy Crust Sponges (Order Homocoela)—form irregular, grayish to brownish crusts over rocks; body wall thin and not folded internally.
Antler Sponges (Order Homocoela)—body branching, more-or-less antlerlike; body wall thin and not folded internally.

Class Hexactinellida (Hyalospongia) (Glass Sponges)

Diagnosis: spicules, or spines, glassy or siliceous (will not dissolve in acid) and 6-rayed; mostly solitary, cylindrical, vase-, urn-, or funnel-shaped animals, but some are curved, flattened, or branched; most are 4–12 inches long, but some are 3 feet long; strictly marine, from 300 feet to 3 miles deep, mostly deep; the only types likely to be dredged are shown.
Venus Flower Basket (Order Hexasterophora)—body long and slender, vaselike.
Glass Rope Sponges (Order Amphidiscophora)—body composed of an expanded and a tail-like part.
Glass Goblet Sponges (Order Amphidiscophora)—body short and broad, gobletlike.

Class Demospongia (Frame Sponges)

Diagnosis: 3 subclasses: Tetractinellida, a shallow-water marine group, lack fibrous spongin in their skeleton and either lack spicules, or spines, or have 4-rayed siliceous ones; Monaxonida, a mostly shallow-water marine group (but extend to over 3-mile depths and include a freshwater family) possess toothpick-like siliceous spicules and some have spongin in their skeletons; Keratosa, usually a shallow-water, hard, marine bottom group (strictly marine, include bath sponges) have skeletons all of fibrous spongin.

Even individual species may vary in form, texture, and color. In this manual, marine forms (coned, warty, tentacled, corrugated, crust, dome, globular, leaf, tree, fin-

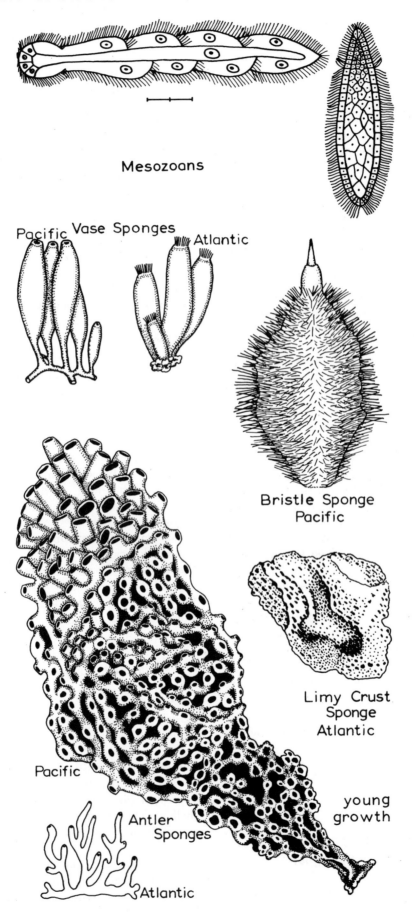

Mesozoans

Vase Sponges

Pacific

Atlantic

Bristle Sponge
Pacific

Limy Crust
Sponge
Atlantic

Pacific

Antler
Sponges

Atlantic

young
growth

GLASS SPONGES

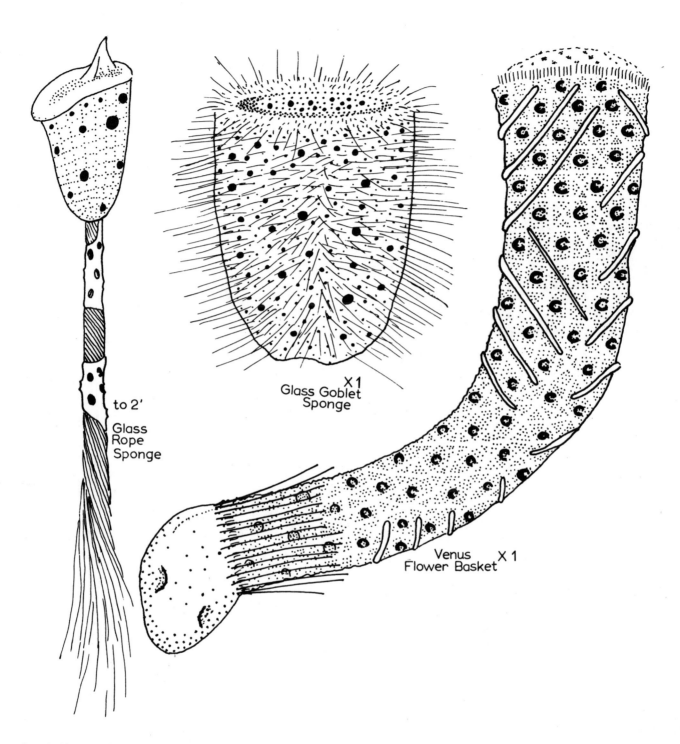

to 2'
Glass
Rope
Sponge

X1
Glass Goblet
Sponge

Venus
Flower Basket X 1

gered, tubular, and goblet) are recognized on the basis of form and texture. The only group of freshwater sponges are named on the basis of their habitat.

COELENTERATA (CNIDARIA)
(COELENTERATES)

Diagnosis: no head or segmentation, tentacles surround the mouth, which leads into a saclike cavity that may be separated by membranes; 2 body forms, the tubular-

bodied, somewhat plantlike *polyp* with mouth and tentacles at one end and attachment at the other, and the umbrella-shaped, usually free-swimming *medusa* with a jellylike body having tentacles on the umbrella margin and mouth on a central projection of the undersurface; polyps mostly sessile, also movably attached to objects or more-or-less buried in gravel, sand, or mud, rarely free-floating; both medusae and polyps are variously modified and both forms appear in the life stages of many species, in the latter case 1 form is small, frequently microscopic,

FRAME SPONGES

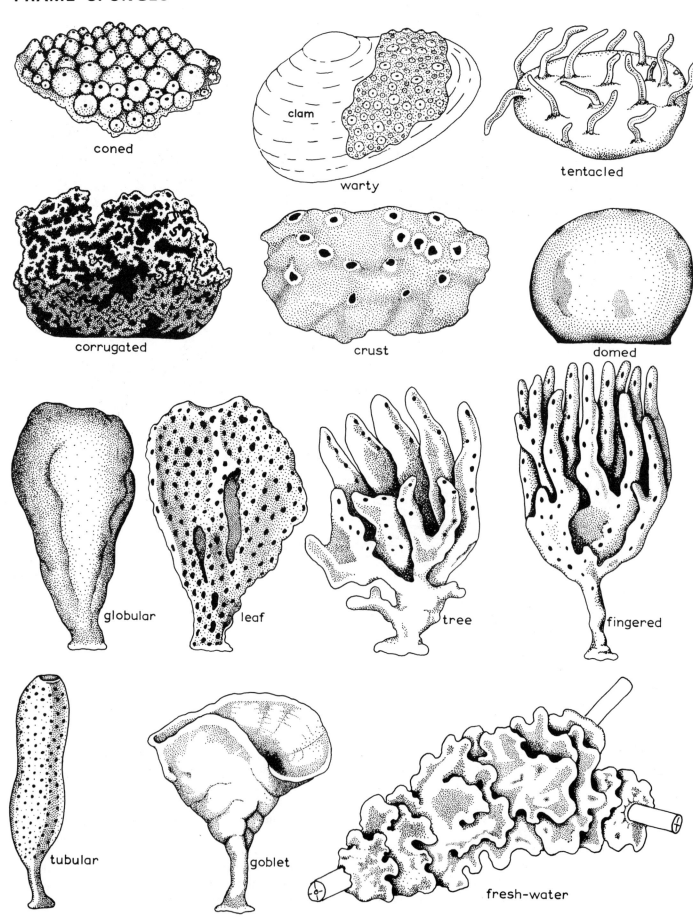

coned

warty

clam

tentacled

corrugated

crust

domed

globular

leaf

tree

fingered

tubular

goblet

fresh-water

hence inconspicuous; solitary as polyps and medusae, or colonial as polyps (rarely as medusae), individual polyps of a colony are usually minute, at least of 2 types, feeding-protective and medusae-forming, feeding and protective may be separate types; many look plantlike, some flower-like, others resemble jellylike umbrellas; many are brightly colored; reproduction generally involving an alternation of generations, asexual polyps bud sexual, bi-parental medusae whose fertilized eggs develop into mobile larvae, the larvae settling to the substrate and developing into a single polyp or colony of polyps; polyps and medusae generally with thread cells (nematocysts) which are variously modified to sting, spear, entangle, or otherwise capture prey or repel predators; marine predators, depending upon coelenterate size, on microorganisms to fish, generally prey is partly immobilized with thread cells before tentacles are used to collect and transport the prey to the mouth.

Coelenterate species having colonial polyps may be confused with plantlike Ectoprocta or Entoprocta. However, the latter are structurally unique and normally have a thin, rough, usually white or whitish crust covering the soft parts of their bodies.

Habitat: mostly marine, also in fresh water; most adults are attached to rocks or organisms, commonly found on seaweeds.

Class Hydrozoa (Hydrozoans)

Diagnosis: solitary or colonial; both asexual polyps and sexual medusae usually present, but one form often is suppressed; polyps without vertical membranes partitioning the internal body cavity; medusae with a velum (a shelf-like membranous ring attached to the inner margin of the "umbrella"); almost entirely marine, a few freshwater species (the only nonmarine coelenterates); although not rare, freshwater species tend to be overlooked.

Note: the classification of two orders, Hydroidea and Trachylina, is largely one of convenience to avoid current taxonomic problems.

Order Hydroidea (Hydroids)

Diagnosis: solitary or colonial plantlike animals; polyp generation well-developed; medusae, if present, are small; marine and freshwater.

Freshwater Hydroids or Hydras (Suborder Gymnoblastea, Family Hydridae)—solitary polyps with tentacles; no medusa stage; freshwater only.

Brackish Water Hydroids (Suborder Gymnoblastea, Family Hydridae)—solitary polyps without tentacles; no medusa stage; brackish water to almost fresh; rare, New England coast.

Colonial Hydroids (Suborders Gymnoblastea and Calyptoblastea)—colonial polyps with or without a minute or microscopic medusa stage; 1 freshwater species (resembles first form figured), otherwise marine.

Fairy Palms (Suborder Gymnoblastea, Family Tubulariidae)—solitary polyps, vaguely palmlike; warmer marine waters, generally in mudflats of bays.

Clam Hydroids (Suborder Calyptoblastea)—colonial polyps attached to clams; medusa stage generally present; marine.

Sea Feathers (Suborder Calyptoblastea)—colonial polyps, organization somewhat featherlike; medusa stage usually present; marine.

Order Trachylina (Hydromedusae)

Diagnosis: polyp generation reduced or absent, medusa the dominant form; many do not possess a polyp stage the stage prior to the medusa being a parasite on the parent or other species of hydromedusan; marine and fresh-water, floating or swimming.

Freshwater Hydromedusae (Suborder Trachymedusae, Family Petasidae)—colonial polyp stage to about .3 inch tall; 1 species, the animal figured with a polyp stage.

Marine Hydromedusae (Suborders Narcomedusae and Trachymedusae)—polyp stage generally absent or smaller than in freshwater hydromedusae.

Order Hydrocoralina (Hydrocorals)

Diagnosis: colonial with the polyp form dominant but also with a massive, calcareous skeleton of coral through which 2 kinds of polyps protrude; coral opening through which polyps protrude generally smaller and simpler-structured than those of other corals; marine.

Encrusting and Branching Hydrocorals (Suborder Stylasterina)—encrusting or branching, generally purplish; shallow water, generally extending from just below low tide level, on rocks.

Stinging Corals (Suborder Milleporina)—irregularly lobed; generally on tropical reefs, including Florida; containing powerful stinging cells.

Order Siphonophora (Siphonophores)

Diagnosis: free-swimming or floating colonies consisting of modified medusoid and polypoid individuals of many sorts.

Portuguese Men-of-War (Suborder Cystonectae)—with a large, hollow, bladderlike float; float often tinted with brilliant colors; tentacles especially long; sting particularly potent, will paralyze prey including large fish, can paralyze, even kill, man; a small fish lives among and lures prey to the tentacles, small fish apparently also feeds on the prey; warm, generally tropical waters; very rare on Pacific Coast of United States, commoner on our Atlantic Coast.

Purple Sailors (Suborder Disconectae)—float chambered, flattened, generally raftlike; float with a keel-like crest; gen-

HYDROZOANS I

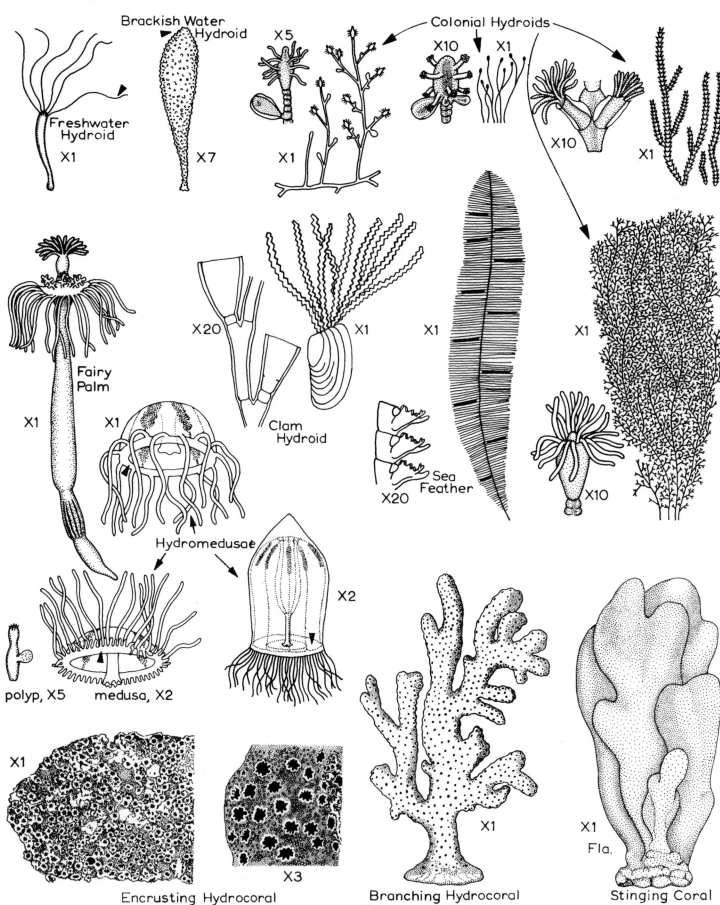

Freshwater Hydroid X1

Brackish Water Hydroid X7

X5

Colonial Hydroids

X10 X1

X10

X1

X1

Fairy Palm

X1

X20

Clam Hydroid X1

X1

X1

Sea Feather X20

X10

Hydromedusae

X1

X2

polyp, X5 medusa, X2

X1

X3

Encrusting Hydrocoral

Branching Hydrocoral X1

Stinging Coral X1 Fla.

erally colored blue-green to purplish blue; often washed up on beaches in great numbers.

Sea Rafts (Suborder Disconectae)—float chambered, flattened, generally raftlike; float without a keel-like crest; generally colored bright blue to green; Atlantic, South Carolina southward.

Bladder Siphonophores (Suborder Calyconectae)— individuals with 1 to a few bladderlike swimming organs.

Bladder Siphonophores (Suborder Physonectae)—individuals with a small float and bladderlike swimming organs, swimming organs in 2 alternating rows.

Class Scyphozoa (Jellyfishes)

Diagnosis: solitary, umbrella- or bell-like medusae; polyp form reduced or absent; medusae without a "shelf" (velum); material between inner and outer tissue layers of body very thick and jellylike; medusa margin regularly with 8 notches that contain sensory organs; strictly marine; all large medusae belong to this class; some of our large species are potentially lethal to man.

Order Stauromedusae (Sessile Jellyfishes)

Diagnosis: attached upside down, usually to kelp or eelgrass; attachment is not permanent, animals can crawl along the substrate; top of umbrella drawn out into an attachment stalk; common species about an inch or more in diameter and are most likely found on eelgrass in quiet waters such as bays.

Order Cubomedusae (Cuboidal Jellyfishes)

Diagnosis: free-swimming; umbrella cuboidal with margin bent inward and with 4 or 4 groups of tentacles; ours along Atlantic shores, mostly in subtropical to tropical waters.

Order Coronatae (Scalloped Jellyfishes)

Diagnosis: free-swimming, umbrella margin scalloped and separated from umbrella proper by a circular furrow; mostly deep-water forms.

Order Semaeostomeae (Four-arm Jellyfishes)

Diagnosis: free-swimming; 4 corners of mouth prolonged as 4 frilly arms; tentacles present; encountered mostly in coastal waters, includes common jellyfishes.

Order Rhizostomeae (Eight-arm Jellyfishes)

Diagnosis: free-swimming; many small mouths among arms, no central mouth; 8 arms; tentacles absent; encountered mostly in coastal waters.

Class Anthozoa (Anthozoans)

Diagnosis: solitary or colonial; strictly polyps, no medusae known; polyps with vertical membranes partitioning the body cavity; strictly marine.

SUBCLASS ALCYONARIA (Alcyonarians)

Diagnosis: with 8 branched tentacles; colonial; with an internal skeleton.

Order Stolonifera (Stolon Corals)

Diagnosis: polyps originate separately from a common, flattened, creeping tube (stolon) or mat; skeleton of spines occurring separately or fused into tubes; polyps usually contracted to small pinkish mounds so the tentacles are not visible; coral base and ribbonlike stolon help separate these animals from simple ascidians (Chordata).

Organ Pipe Corals (Family Tubiporidae)—extralimital on coral reefs in tropical waters, frequently found in curio shops and museums.

Stolon Corals (Family Clavulariidae)—mostly in deeper water, intertidal species form low, encrusting, spreading growths on rocks, shells, or other hard substrates.

Order Telestacea (False Stolon Corals)

Diagnosis: colonial, of simple or branched stem bearing lateral polyps; each colony stem grows erect from a somewhat stemlike creeping base; internal skeletal parts united or not; mostly in deep water.

Order Alcyonacea (Soft Corals)

Diagnosis: lower polyp parts fused into a fleshy mass but upper parts free; skeletal parts neither united nor axial; mostly shallow water of warm shores, subtidal to fairly deep waters.

Order Gorgonacea (Horny Corals)

Diagnosis: colony plantlike, originating from a single base; supported by a central coral skeleton or hornlike material or both; polyps originate from each side of the skeleton, but no polyp reaches the colony base.

Gorgons (All Gorgonacea except 1 genus)—colony branching, treelike; mostly tropical and subtropical subtidal waters, one occurs at Newport Bay, California.

Sea Fans (Gorgonia)—colony branching but branches connected and in 1 plane, fanlike; tropical waters.

Order Pennatulacea (Sea Whips, Sea Pens, and Sea Pansies)

Diagnosis: colony somewhat featherlike, feather-dusterlike, or leaflike; polyps borne on a very long, stemlike polyp, the stalk; stalk usually embedded in sand or mud; skeleton of separate spines; occur on soft bottoms, mostly in warm waters, frequently found in shallow waters in bays.

Sea Whips (12 Families)—polyps borne in groups or variously arranged on each side of a very long, stemlike

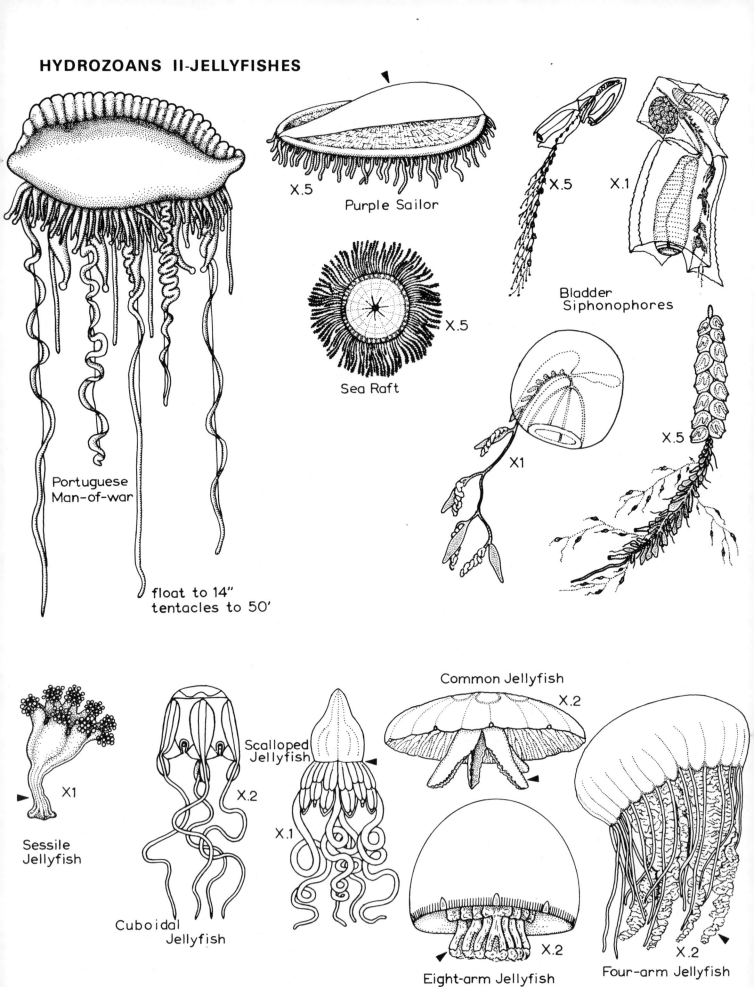

X.5
Purple Sailor

X.5

X.1

Bladder
Siphonophores

X.5

Sea Raft

X1

X.5

Portuguese
Man-of-war

float to 14"
tentacles to 50'

X1

Sessile
Jellyfish

Cuboidal
Jellyfish

X.2

Scalloped
Jellyfish

X.1

Common Jellyfish

X.2

X.2

Eight-arm Jellyfish

X.2

Four-arm Jellyfish

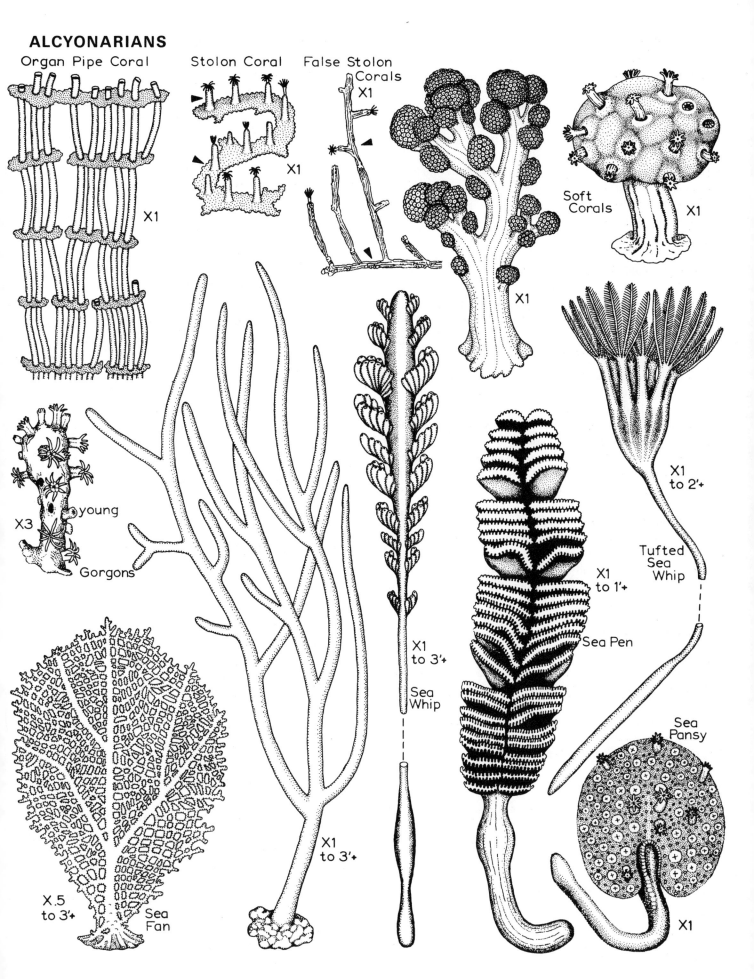

ALCYONARIANS

Organ Pipe Coral

Stolon Coral

False Stolon Corals
X1

X1

X1

X1

Soft Corals
X1

X3 young

Gorgons

X1 to 3'+

Sea Whip

X1 to 1'+

Sea Pen

X1 to 2'+

Tufted Sea Whip

Sea Pansy

X1

X.5 to 3'+

Sea Fan

X1 to 3'+

polyp; colony whiplike; generally on muddy bottoms of shallow waters, in bays and deeper waters.

Sea Pens (Family Pennatulidae)—polyps borne in groups on each side of a very long, stemlike polyp; colony featherlike; generally 300–3000 feet deep.

Tufted Sea Whips (Family Umbellulidae)—polyps borne at apex of a very long, stemlike polyp; colony whiplike; deep sea.

Sea Pansies (Family Renillidae)—polyps borne on upper surface of a leaflike structure, stalk soft; color reddish, bluish, or purplish; shallow warm waters, generally bays, may be uncovered by lowest low tides.

SUBCLASS ZOANTHARIA (Sea Anemones and Stony Corals)

Diagnosis: tentacles of various numbers, but never 8; solitary or colonial; with or without a skeleton.

Order Actiniaria (Burrowing and Sea Anemones)

Diagnosis: solitary but some closely grouped; no skeleton; polyp columnar, base a suction disc or a pointed, rounded, or bulblike structure.

Burrowing Anemones (Family Edwardsiidae)—body with 8 longitudinal ridges, base without a suction disc; 1 circlet of tentacles; generally burrow in sand or sandy mud in bays, sometimes under rocks, often encrusted with sand, rarely comb jelly parasites when young; shallow water.

Sea Anemones (many families)—body smooth or ridged, never with only 8 longitudinal ridges, base with or without a suction disc; tentacles in 2 or more circlets or in radiating rows; generally on substrate objects or floating objects such as buoys, also under rocks or in crevices, often encrusted with shells; intertidal to deep water.

Order Ceriantharia (Tube Anemones)

Diagnosis: solitary; polyps long, slender, and anemonelike but never with a suction disc; many tentacles arranged in 2 unlike circlets; construct black, often slimy, parchmentlike tubes up to 6 or more feet long; mostly burrowing forms in sand or mud; usually only the tentacles and mouth are visible on the surface, even when the animals are not disturbed; intertidal to continental slope.

Order Zoanthidea (False or Colonial Sea Anemones)

Diagnosis: mostly colonial, with polyps united by basal stolons; solitary forms have a stalked or wedge-shaped base; neither skeletons nor basal suction discs; generally subtidal shallow water, many grow upon invertebrates.

Order Madreporaria (Stony Corals)

Diagnosis: mostly colonial; skeleton present; polyps small in cups of coral skeletons; mostly in warm, shallow waters; main contributors to coral reefs.

Solitary Stony Corals—solitary, coral cups not joined in a closely associated, single mass.

Colonial Stony Corals—colonial, coral cups intimately joined into a single mass; except for Florida waters, the commonest shallow-water and only Pacific type in our area is encrusting or essentially so; deeper Atlantic waters have branching types; Florida, especially the Keys, has a great variety of types in reefs.

Order Antipatharia (Black or Thorny Corals)

Diagnosis: colonial, plantlike; skeleton present; stemlike parts of horny material bearing small, 6-tentacled polyps; extralimital, deep tropical waters, closest in West Indies.

CTENOPHORA (COMB JELLIES)

Diagnosis: body more-or-less spherical, the general appearance resulting in the common name of "sea gooseberries" or "sea walnuts," or flat and beltlike; jellyfishlike in the sense of being gelatinous and semitransparent but have 8 external rows of comb plates and are not of medusoid form; predaceous, feeding mostly on eggs and larvae of larger animals.
Habitat: all free-swimming and marine.
Sea Gooseberries—body oval to spherical.
Sea Walnuts—body somewhat compressed or thimblelike.
Venus's Girdles—body ribbonlike.

PLATYHELMINTHES (FLATWORMS)

Diagnosis: wormlike, body unsegmented, soft and usually much flattened from top to bottom; includes the free-living flatworms (some resemble ribbonworms), the tapeworms (unique in having a chain of pseudosegments), and the flukes (some resemble leeches).

Free-living flatworms have indications of most of the external features of ribbonworms but are flatter, much simpler-structured and lack a proboscis or snout. Flukes appear simpler-structured than leeches, lacking the ringed body and suckers at both ends of the body found in leeches.
Habitat: free-living flatworms are mostly free-living in marine, freshwater, and moist land environments; tapeworms and flukes are internal animal parasites.

Class Turbellaria (Free-living Flatworms)

Diagnosis: regularly free-living; most under 1/5 inch in length but some reach 20 inches; body undivided, covered by epidermis with short, hairlike structures (cilia), no impervious covering (cuticle) or suckers; mouth near middle of the undersurface; mostly free-living carnivores, also commensals or parasites; found in freshwater, marine, and moist land (especially greenhouses) environments.

SEA ANEMONES-STONY CORALS

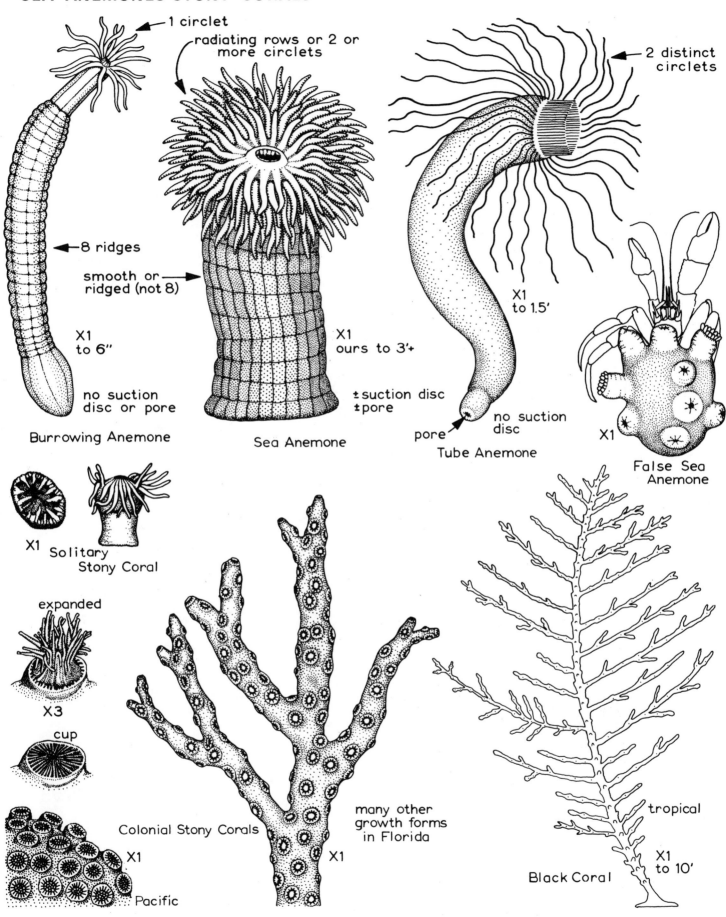

1 circlet

radiating rows or 2 or more circlets

2 distinct circlets

8 ridges

smooth or ridged (not 8)

X1 to 6"

no suction disc or pore

Burrowing Anemone

X1 ours to 3'+

±suction disc ±pore

Sea Anemone

X1 to 1.5'

pore

no suction disc

Tube Anemone

X1

False Sea Anemone

X1 Solitary Stony Coral

expanded

X3

cup

many other growth forms in Florida

Colonial Stony Corals

X1

X1

Pacific

tropical

X1 to 10'

Black Coral

47

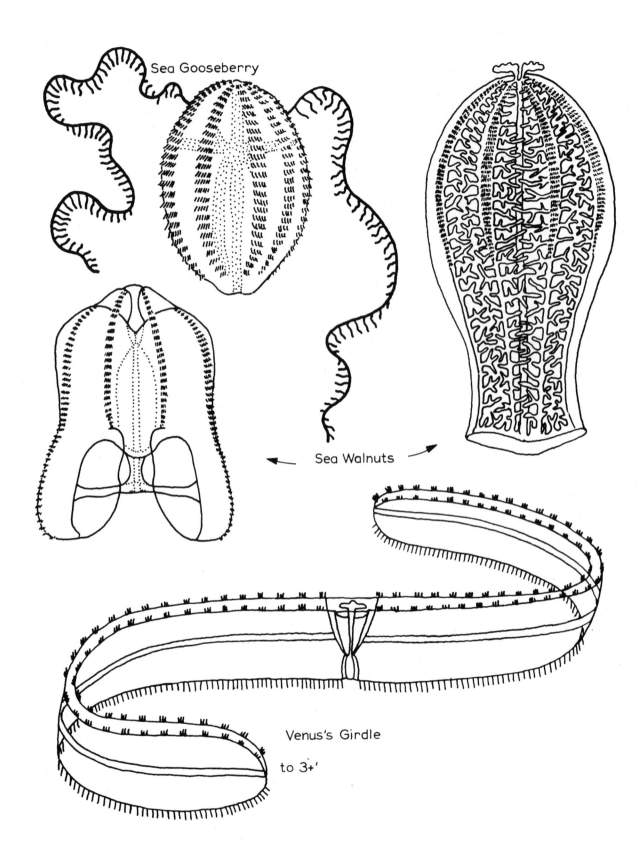

Sea Gooseberry

Sea Walnuts

Venus's Girdle

to 3+′

FLATWORMS

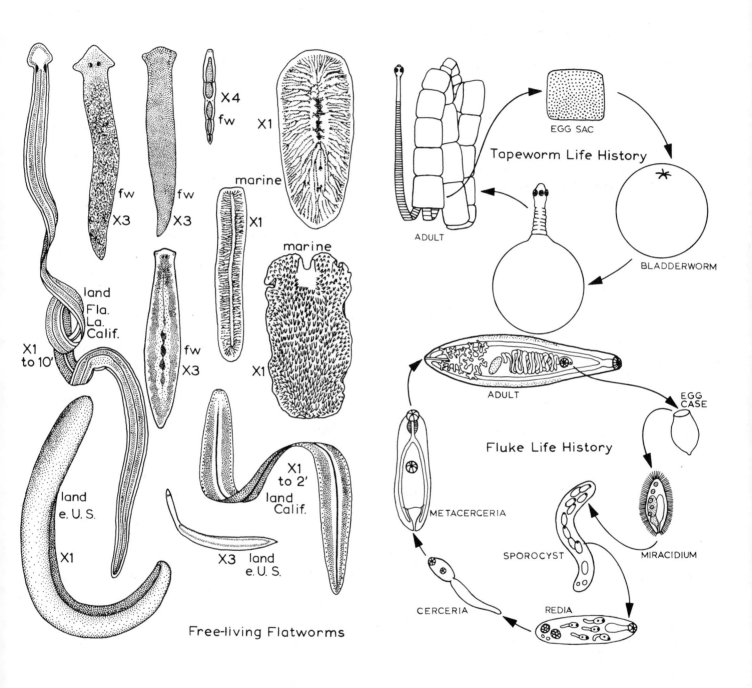

fw

X3

fw

X3

X4
fw

X1
marine

X1

land
Fla.
La.
Calif.

X1
to 10'

fw
X3

X1
marine

X1

land
e. U.S.

X1

X3
land
e.U. S.

X1
to 2'
land
Calif.

Free-living Flatworms

EGG SAC

Tapeworm Life History

BLADDERWORM

ADULT

ADULT

EGG
CASE

Fluke Life History

METACERCERIA

MIRACIDIUM

SPOROCYST

CERCERIA

REDIA

Class Cestoda (Tapeworms)

Diagnosis: strictly parasitic; body divided into proglottids which are not true segments, covered by a protective layer, a cuticle, but no epidermis or cilia; attachment often involves suckers, but also involves adhesive grooves or hooks; adults are vertebrate intestinal parasites.

Class Trematoda (Flukes)

Diagnosis: strictly parasitic; body undivided, covered by a protective layer, a cuticle, one or more suckers, but no epidermis or cilia; mouth typically anterior; internal and external parasites of animals.

NEMERTEA (NEMERTINEA; RHYNCHOCOELA) (RIBBONWORMS)

Diagnosis: wormlike, body unsegmented, soft and highly contractile, cylindrical to flattened; above the mouth a soft proboscis or snout may extend far out or be completely withdrawn like inverting the finger of a glove, leaving only a pore to hint its presence; variously colored, red, brown, yellow, green, or white, some solidly colored and others striped or crossbanded; generally biparental, with or without a larval stage, a few asexual by fragmentation; predators.

The proboscis or its site of origin separates ribbonworms from the somewhat similarly appearing free-living flatworms.

Habitat: almost all marine, a very few are freshwater (1 species in our area), terrestrial, or perhaps parasitic; our freshwater species about 3/4-inch long, whitish to yellowish, yellow or red, rarely green, commonest in fall on aquatic plants, especially algae; commonest in temperate seas under objects, among seaweeds, or in mud, sand, or gravel; some construct tubes which are stabilized by a mucous lining secreted and applied by the worm, some also burrow but form no tubes; a very few are commensals, living in sponges, bivalve mollusks, tunicates, or crabs, none known definitely to be parasitic.

ACANTHOCEPHALA (SPINY-HEADED WORMS)

Diagnosis: wormlike, body unsegmented, usually elongate, flattened, and rough in life (rounded and smoother in preserved specimens); an anterior snout, or proboscis, can be withdrawn into a sheath; proboscis with hooks or spines; life cycle complex with many larval stages, biparental.

Habitat: all are parasites, larvae in arthropods, adults in intestines of vertebrates.

ASCHELMINTHES (CAVITY WORMS)

Diagnosis: wormlike, body unsegmented; includes several groups of mostly slender, small to microscopic species; readily visible species are earthwormlike but smooth and without an external ringed or segmented appearance; generally biparental, some fork-tailed worms hermaphroditic, most rotifers parthenogenetic or seasonally so, larvae present except in fork-tailed worms and rotifers.

Minute to microscopic forms include rotifers (body somewhat cylindrical with an anterior group of cilia, a wheel organ, and posterior forked foot), fork-tailed worms (protozoanlike, ciliate, but the posterior end is forked and the arched top surface has many spines, and spiny-crowned worms (body of 13 or 14 rings, 2 rings form the head which is encircled by spines and has a short, retractile snout terminated by the mouth; trunk rings bear long spines). The three known species of club worms are cylindrical, clublike, yellow or brown, wormlike creatures (superficially resembling peanutworms or spoonworms, but having rows of spines or papillae on the anterior, retractile snout and usually 1 or 2 posterior processes with gill-like outgrowths). Roundworms and horsehair worms are wormlike, unsegmented animals having elongate, slender, cylindrical bodies. Roundworms have their bodies pointed at both ends. Horsehair worms tend to be much longer and thinner (hairlike) than roundworms and not to be pointed at both ends.

Habitat: rotifers are mostly marine, some occur in fresh water and a few are parasites; horsehair worm larvae are insect parasites, adults occur in fresh water; roundworms are free-living in water and on land and are parasitic on plants and animals; fork-tailed worms are aquatic; and both spiny-crowned and club worms are strictly marine.

Class Rotatoria (Rotifers or Wheel Animals)

Diagnosis: microscopic to minute; body somewhat cylindrical with an anterior group of cilia ("wheel organ") and posterior forked "foot;" most are free-living with some fixed in protective tubes; a few parasites; mostly marine, a few freshwater species; mostly parthenogenic; predators on microorganisms, generally trapping prey with the wheel organ, movement of cilia upon this organ is generally involved in drawing prey to the mouth.

Class Nematomorpha (Horsehair Worms)

Diagnosis: about .1–40 inches long; long and slender with a uniformly cylindrical body, a bluntly rounded anterior end and a more-or-less tapered posterior end; body smooth or with 2 rows of bristles; external resistant surface opaque and often colored; most adults in fresh water, often ponds,

RIBBONWORMS-SPINY-HEADED WORMS

Ribbonworms

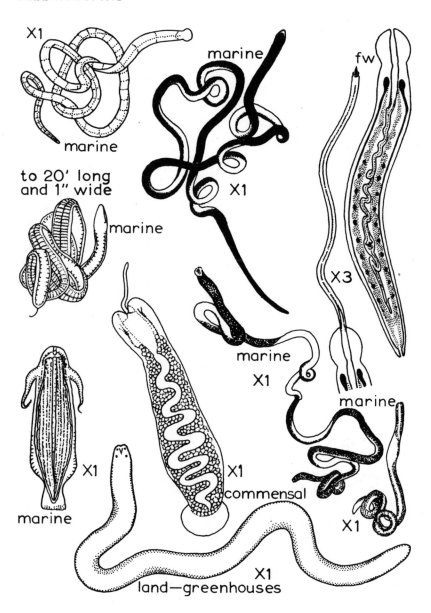

X1

marine

marine

to 20' long
and 1" wide

marine

fw

X3

marine

X1

marine

marine

X1

X1

commensal

land—greenhouses

X1

Spiny-headed Worm

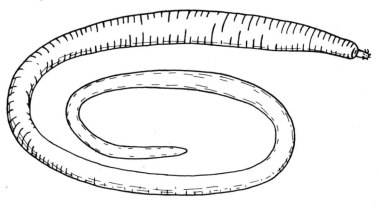

WHEEL ANIMALS-HORSEHAIR WORMS

Wheel Animals (all microscopic and aquatic)

Freshwater Horsehair Worm
X1
to 3'+

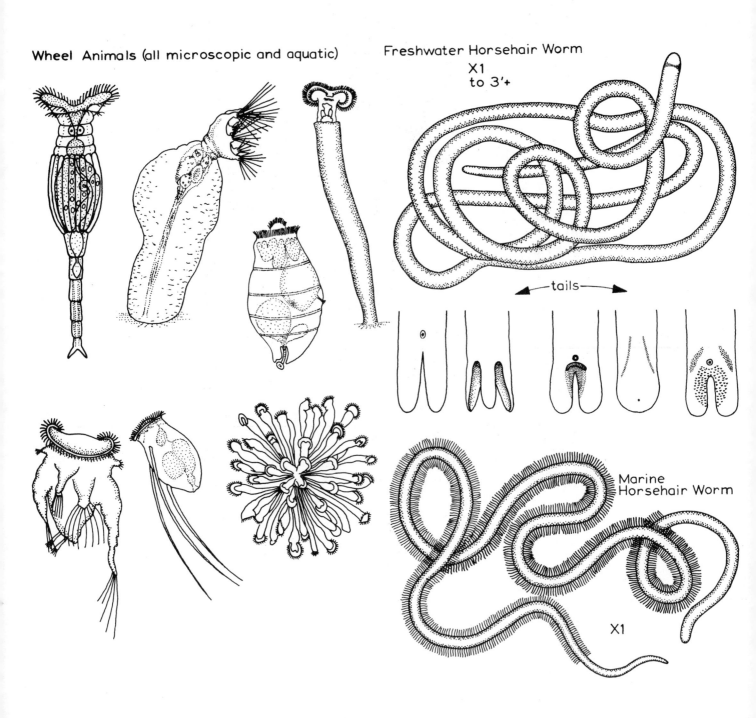

← tails →

Marine
Horsehair Worm

X1

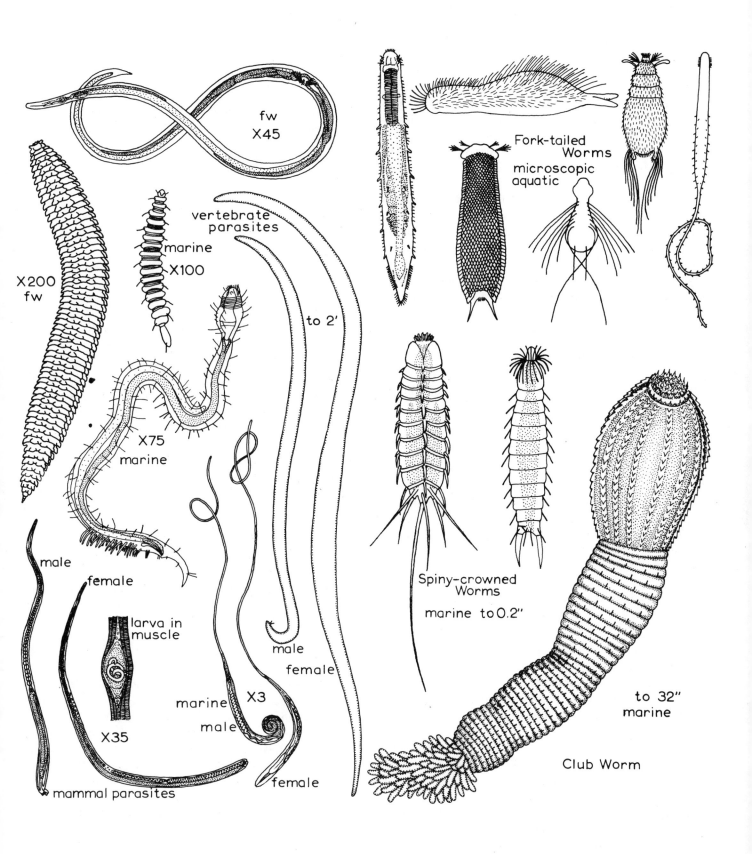

fw
X45

X200
fw

vertebrate
parasites

marine
X100

to 2'

X75
marine

Fork-tailed
Worms
microscopic
aquatic

male

female

larva in
muscle

marine   X3

male

X35

male

female

mammal parasites

male

female

Spiny-crowned
Worms

marine to 0.2"

to 32"
marine

Club Worm

rain puddles, or drinking troughs (adults' horsehair appearance and occurrence in horse troughs led to myth of origin from horses' hairs); adults do not feed, females deposit strings of eggs on objects in fresh water, larva either enters insect larva or encysts on herbs (if encysting, larva enters adult host when insect, crustacean, or mollusk eats herbs), larva transforms to adult horsehair worm within insect (usually a beetle, grasshopper, or cricket) or other host, when host dies in water, adult horsehair worm leaves dead host, entering freshwater environment; marine adults pelagic, biparental, eggs deposited in open sea, larva enters crab body cavity and becomes a parasite, larva transforms to adult within crab host, and adult emerges from host.

Freshwater Horsehair Worms (Order Gordioidea)—body smooth, without bristles; 2 families, Gordiidae with 1 genus, *Gordius*, characterized by a blunt rear end that has a crescentic fold posterior to the cloaca, and Chordodidae with 6 genera in our area.

Marine Horsehair Worms (Order Nectonematoidea)—part of body length with 2 rows of short bristles; 1 genus, *Nectonema*.

Class Nematoda (Roundworms)

Diagnosis: minute to 3+ feet long, most small or minute; unsegmented roundworms with slender, cylindrical bodies that often taper toward both ends, generally not bluntly rounded anteriorly (some appear segmented but usually are not distinctly bristled as are possibly confusing segmented worms); covered by a resistant cuticle; probably 2nd to the insects in numbers of species and individuals (could be more numerous); widespread, free-living on land and in water, parasitic in plants and animals; includes some of the most dangerous human parasites in North America.

Class Gastrotricha (Fork-tailed Worms)

Diagnosis: all microscopic; ciliate, protozoanlike, but the posterior end is forked and the arched top surface has many spines; found in fresh and salt water; freshwater species are parthenogenetic females; marine species hermaphroditic; feed on microorganisms.

Class Kinorhyncha (Spiny-crowned Worms)

Diagnosis: .04–.2 inch long; body of 13 or 14 rings, 2 rings forming the head which is encircled by spines and which has a short, retractile snout terminated by the mouth; the trunk rings bear lateral spines; the tail region may bear long spines; exclusively marine, rarely collected

and poorly known, known to occur in bottom mud or sand and on algae, usually in shallow water; sexes separate, development with several larval stages and changes in form to the adult stage.

Class Priapuloidea (Club Worms)

Diagnosis: mostly to 6 inches long; only 3 known species, rarely dredged; cylindrical, clublike, yellow or brown, wormlike creatures; superficially resemble Sipunculoidea or Echiuroidea, but club worms have rows of spines or papillae on the anterior retractile snout and usually 1 or 2 posterior processes with gill-like outgrowths; intertidal to shallow sea burrowers in bottom mud, mostly of colder to Arctic seas, known only from Belgian and Boston coasts north, Tomales Bay, California, and from Patagonia to Antarctica; sexes separate, development essentially direct but involving a larval stage.

ENTOPROCTA (CROWN ANIMALS)

Diagnosis: along with crest animals once called bryozoans or moss animals; body unsegmented; sessile animals with a circlet of ciliated tentacles (lophophore) around the mouth; superficial resemblance to hydroids and seaweeds but internal structure is much more complex, closer resemblance to crest animals and were formerly joined with them into a single phylum, but only crown animals can move their individual stalks independently; adults biparental or hermaphroditic, egg develops into a motile larva which transforms to the adult form; filter feeders on microorganisms.

Habitat: ours mostly marine, our only freshwater species occurs from Texas to the Great Lakes to Pennsylvania, Kentucky, and Virginia.

Annelid's Crown Animals (Family Loxosomatidae)—solitary, stalk attached by an adhesive disc; individuals bud from an adult's body; marine commensals, generally upon marine segmented worms, also found on peanut worms, sponges, ascidians, and less frequently, on other marine animals.

Freshwater Crown Animals (Family Urnatellidae)—our only freshwater crown animals; colonial, a small colony arising from a basal plate; 1 genus, *Urnatella*.

Stolon Crown Animals (Family Pedicellinidae)—colonial, groups of stalked individuals arising from a basal, stemlike stolon; growth form tends to emphasize the runner-like stolon; upright branching not extensive; individual stalks relatively heavy and of uniform thickness.

Branching Crown Animals (Family Pedicellinidae)—colonial groups of stalked individuals arising from a basal, stemlike stolon; growth form tends to emphasize branching of the stalks; individual stalks slender, tending to expand slightly toward body of the individual animal.

CROWN ANIMALS

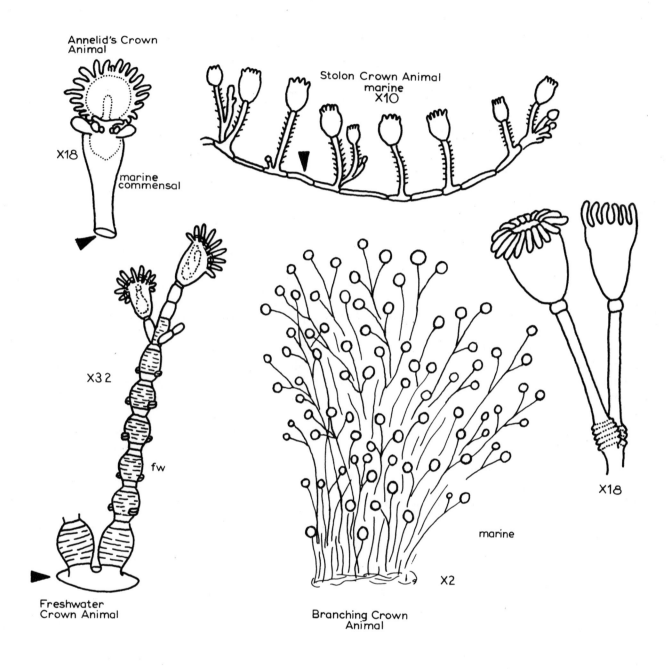

Annelid's Crown
Animal

X18

marine
commensal

Stolon Crown Animal
marine
X10

X32

fw

Freshwater
Crown Animal

Branching Crown
Animal

marine

X2

X18

ECTOPROCTA (CREST ANIMALS)

Diagnosis: along with crown animals were at one time generally called bryozoans or moss animals; body unsegmented; sessile or free-floating colonial animals with a circlet of ciliated tentacles (lophophore) around the mouth; many colonies are tufted or branched, others resemble colonial hydroids, corals, or seaweeds, a few are matlike and some form thin crusts on rocks, seaweeds, shells, etc.; crusts generally whitish, yellowish, or brick red; likely to be overlooked because most are small and inconspicuous, but some attain considerable size; although referred to as moss animals, few are mosslike; closest resemblance to crown animals, but few crest animals have any semblance of a stalk, which only in crown animals is contractile; usually hermaphroditic, some biparental, egg develops into a motile larva which transforms into the adult.

Habitat: mostly marine; freshwater forms tend to be gelatinous, some exceedingly so.

Class Stenolaemata

Diagnosis: lophophore circular, upon a structure that does not overhang body; body coverings calcareous, at least partly distinct, tubular, with opening at, or nearly at, upper end; tube openings more-or-less circular, lack a lid; strictly marine, intertidal forms on rocks and organisms.

Sea Tubes (Order Cyclostomata)—erect or partly so, treelike, fanlike, or flattened but branched.

Sea Lichens (Order Cyclostomata)—encrusting, fanlike to circular.

Class Gymnolaemata

Diagnosis: lophophore circular, upon a structure that does not overhang body; body coverings calcareous, leathery, soft, or jellylike, if calcareous, rarely as distinct tubes, openings towards upper end but distinctly on "front" rather than end; tube openings generally not circular, closed by a lid; mostly marine.

Sea Lace (Order Chilostomata)—body coverings calcareous; colony flat, erect, netlike, ruffled.

Sea Leaves (Order Chilostomata)—body coverings calcareous; colony flat, erect, of leaflike lobes.

Sea Gall (Order Chilostomata)—body coverings calcareous; colony encrusting.

Moss Animals (Order Chilostomata)—body coverings calcareous; colony erect, branching plantlike, including treelike, shrublike, mosslike, or algaelike.

Coraline Crest Animals (Order Chilostomata)—body covering calcareous or chitinous (soft); colony erect, irregularly branched, not plantlike.

Gooseneck Crest Animals (Order Chilostomata)—individuals in clublike coverings, arise from a stemlike structure.

Tubular Crest Animals (Order Ctenostomata)—body coverings soft; colony consisting of a stolon (stemlike runner) giving rise to erect, tubular individuals; marine forms generally inconspicuous, appear as fuzz on animals or rock surfaces; freshwater forms inconspicuous and rare, known only from southeastern Pennsylvania rapid streams, on rocks.

Bristly Sea Fingers (Order Ctenostomata)—body coverings gelatinous; colony erect, and branching or flat; encrust algae, animals (especially crabs), and rocks.

Jointed Crest Animals (Order Ctenostomata)—body coverings soft; colony consisting of individuals in club-shaped coverings joined end to end, individuals distinct from one another; strictly freshwater, in standing and slow-moving water.

Class Phylactolaemata

Diagnosis: lophophore U-shaped, oval, or circular, partly borne on a structure that overlaps body; body coverings mostly soft, leathery or jellylike, also firm, sometimes horny; strictly freshwater; 1 order, Plumatellina.

Crest Animal Worms (Family Cristatellidae)—colony soft, transparent, jellylike, somewhat wormlike; generally on upper side of submerged objects, in standing or slow-moving fresh water; small colonies may creep, but imperceptibly, to 4 inches per day.

Branching Crest Animals (Family Plumatellidae)—colony soft to firm, jellylike to horny, erect and branching; generally on submerged plants in quiet or standing water.

Crest Animal Pipes (Family Plumatellidae)—colony soft, jellylike, erect, not branching, often saclike and lobed; usually on plants in standing water.

Jelly Crest Animals (Family Lophopodidae)—colony soft, transparent, jellylike, globular or lobed; individuals generally confined to surface of large jellylike mass; generally on submerged objects in shaded, standing water.

PHORONIDA (HORSESHOE FANWORMS)

Diagnosis: wormlike, body unsegmented; red, orange, or green animals from under .1 inch to 15 inches long (tubes to 18 inches); live in self-secreted, leathery, membranous, or calcareous tubes containing cemented sand grains, shells, and other materials; superficially resemble some of the annelids (feather duster and tentacle worms), but the "fan" (lophophore) is of horseshoe shape, and the body is smooth and segmented; hermaphroditic, egg develops into a larva which in turn transforms into the adult; filter feeders; 2 genera and 15 species.

Habitat: shallow water marine; sedentary tube dwellers on sand or mud bottoms, generally encountered in bays or estuaries.

CREST ANIMALS

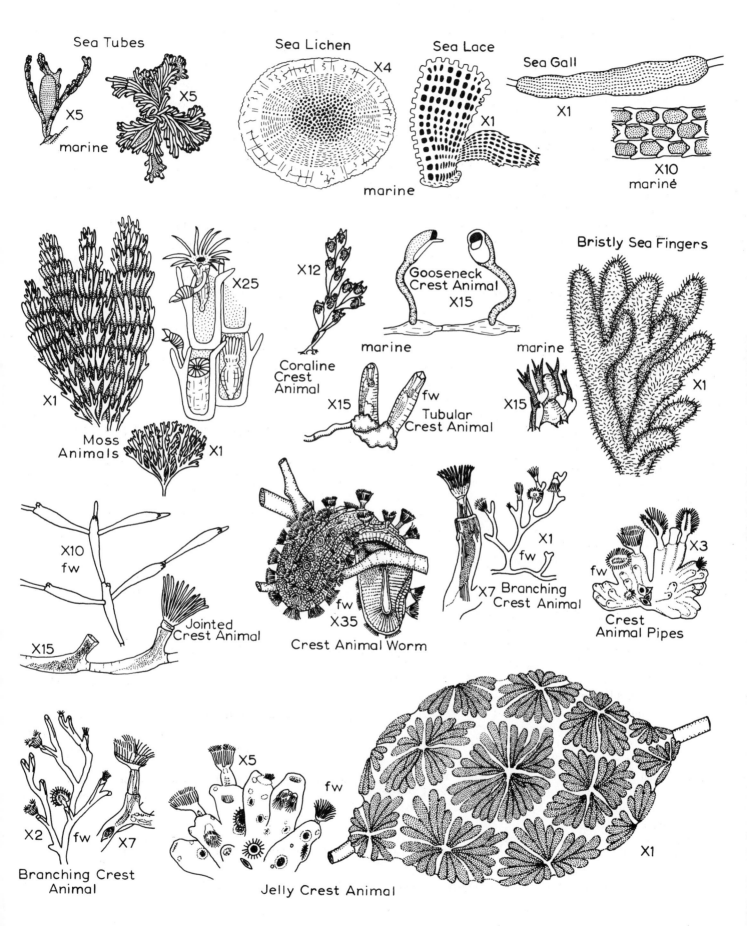

Sea Tubes
X5
marine
X5

Sea Lichen
X4
marine

Sea Lace
X1

Sea Gall
X1
X10
marine

X25

X12
Coraline Crest Animal

Gooseneck Crest Animal
X15
marine

Bristly Sea Fingers
X1

X1
Moss Animals
X1

X15
fw
Tubular Crest Animal

marine
X15

X10
fw

X15
Jointed Crest Animal

fw
X35
Crest Animal Worm

X1
fw
X7 Branching Crest Animal

X3
fw
Crest Animal Pipes

X2 fw X7
Branching Crest Animal

X5
fw
Jelly Crest Animal

X1

BRACHIOPODA (LAMP SHELLS)

Diagnosis: clamlike, body unsegmented, and covered by a bivalve shell, but valves are top and bottom; a flexible attachment stalk emerges through a hole in the bottom valve near the hinge; common name refers to the resemblance of some shells to old Roman lamps; solitary; biparental, egg to mobile larva to adult; filter feeders on microorganisms.

Lamp shells superficially resemble bivalve mollusks but have top and bottom valves rather than right and left, and are unique in having both a stalk and a normal opening in the lower valve.

Habitat: strictly marine, sometimes intertidal but to 3+ miles deep; most are attached under or on rocks (also on other firm substrates), but some excavate and live in vertical burrows in mud or sand.

SIPUNCULOIDEA (SIPUNCULIDA) (PEANUT WORMS)

Diagnosis: body unsegmented, wormlike; cylindrical, yellowish, grayish, or brownish, but generally drab-colored, tentacled worms; anterior region, including tentacles, withdraws inward as does the finger of a glove; called peanut worms owing to peanutlike appearance of the adult when anterior portion is pulled into the body; biparental, egg to mobile larva to adult; detritus feeders.

Peanut worms superficially resemble club worms and spoonworms but the anterior retractile portion of peanut worms is terminated by tentacles and is not a true snout, or proboscis.

Habitat: marine burrowers in sand or mud but do not build tubes; also live in empty shells, crevices in rocks, etc.; intertidal to about 3-mile depths, generally sedentary.

MOLLUSCA (MOLLUSKS)

Diagnosis: body unsegmented, with or without a shell, of diverse forms; a rasplike radula, used in obtaining food, is typical of all classes except Pelecypoda; monoplacophorans resemble some univalves (limpets); tusk shells also resemble some univalves (snails) but have a tubular shell open at both ends; chitons, except for deep sea worm-like forms, are of elliptical outline, have a large, flat, ventral foot, and a shell of 8 overlapping dorsal valves, or plates, that may be covered by the skin; univalves are snail- or sluglike, having a 1-piece shell or none at all; bivalves are clamlike (shell of 2 parts, or valves); squids and octupi have an internal shell.

Only bivalves and worm chitons are likely to be confused with other animals. Bivalves resemble lamp shells but have right and left valves instead of top and bottom and are not stalked. Worm chitons are distinctive in appearance, have fine, limy spicules, or spines, in the body covering (the only indication of a shell), and may or may not have a ventral foot.

Habitat: freshwater, marine, land (damp soil usually), and parasitic.

Class Monoplacophora (Monoplacophorans)

Diagnosis: bilaterally symmetrical; shell undivided, oval, external, to 1.6 inches long; 5–6 pairs of external gills distributed on each side of a ventral foot; deep sea; biparental, egg to mobile larva to adult.

Class Scaphopoda (Tusk or Tooth Shells)

Diagnosis: bilaterally symmetrical; body elongate and enclosed in an undivided shell that is open at both ends, with a head area including sensory processes, and with a reduced, conical foot; marine, burrowers in sand or mud, mostly deeper water (to 6,000 feet), but a few are found just below the lowest tide level; biparental, egg to mobile larva to adult; feed on microorganisms, using tentacles to capture food.

Class Amphineura (Chitons or Sea Cradles)

Diagnosis: bilaterally symmetrical; body elongate, with a reduced head and an enlarged, flat, ventral foot (sometimes absent); shell of 8 dorsal parts (valves); shell and sometimes foot absent in worm chitons, a distinctive group of wormlike animals having fine, limy spicules in the body covering; biparental, hermaphroditic in some worm chitons, egg to mobile larva to adult; mostly herbivorous, generally scrape algae from rocks with their radulae, also carnivorous or parasitic.

SUBCLASS APLACOPHORA (Worm Chitons)

Diagnosis: wormlike, about 1 inch long; skin with calcareous spicules, no shell; Atlantic, deep water.
Worm Chitons (Order Chaetodermomorpha)—body cylindrical, without foot or ventral groove; sand and mud burrowers; predaceous, especially on marine segmented worms.
Parasitic Chitons (Order Neomeniomorpha)—body with foot and ventral groove; parasites, especially on hydroids and corals.

SUBCLASS POLYPLACOPHORA (True Chitons)

Diagnosis: body oval, flattened; shell present, of 8

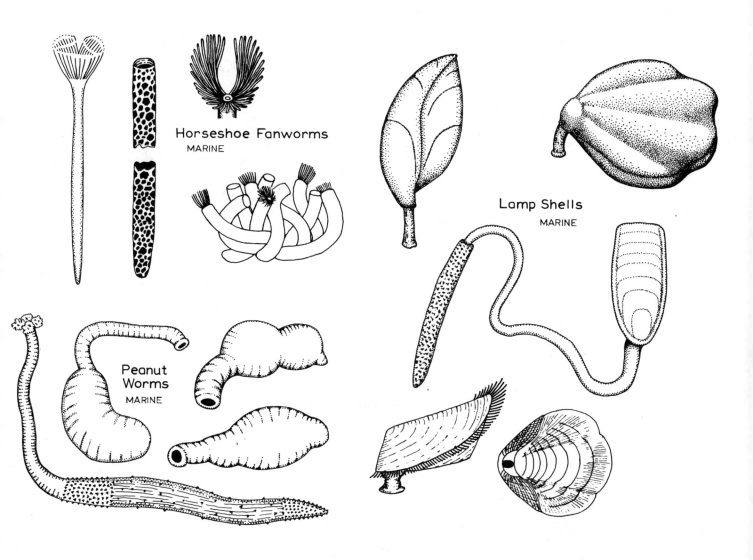

Horseshoe Fanworms
MARINE

Lamp Shells
MARINE

Peanut
Worms
MARINE

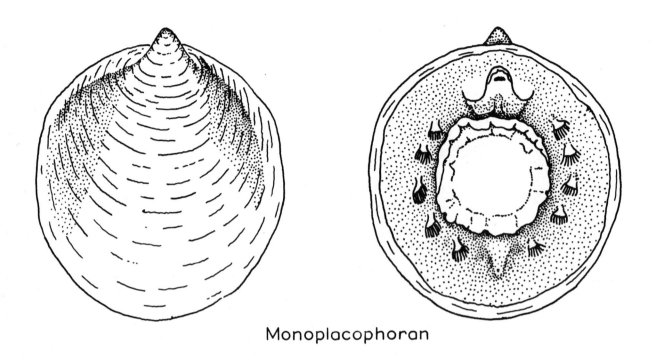

Monoplacophoran

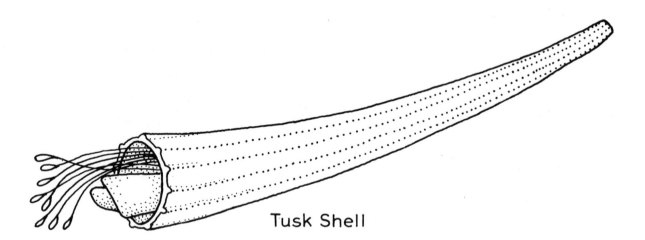

Tusk Shell

valves, ranging from free to hidden under body covering (mantle or girdle); specialized for adhering to rocks and other solid substrates, body has little resistance to wave shock; generally on or under rocks, intertidal to continental slope; often called sea cradles owing to position assumed when removed from rocks, chain-of-mail shells owing to scales present on the mantle of some, and butterfly shells (applied to individual valves) owing to the butterfly shape of individual parts of the shell.

Order Lepidopleurida

Diagnosis: valves completely exposed, at least 2nd through last without a lower edge part (insertion plate) that is covered by the inner edge of the mantle; mantle narrow; ours strictly subtidal, below 100 feet, Oregon to Bering Sea and Gulf of Maine to Greenland.

Cancellate Chitons (Family Lepidopleuridae)—girdle narrow, scaled; scales tiny, overlapping, densely packed, split-pea shaped, but girdle margin has some club-shaped to fine, mosslike scales.

Order Chitonida

Diagnosis: valves exposed or not; insertion plate present; all families with both subtidal and intertidal representatives.

Girdled Chitons (Family Acanthochitonidae)—valves partly covered by girdle.

Giant Chitons (Family Acanthochitonidae)—valves completely covered by girdle; Pacific.

Veiled Chitons (Family Mopalidae)—center rear margin of posterior valve has broad notch; girdle expanded in front; ours, Monterey, California and south.

Notched Chitons (Family Mopalidae)—center rear margin of posterior valve with a broad notch; girdle not expanded in front.

Slender Chitons (Family Ishnochitonidae)—insertion plates with outer edges slit into teeth (best viewed from below); girdle naked and leathery, finely granulated, scaled, or short and rigid-spined.

Tropical Chitons (Family Chitonidae)—insertion plates with outer edges finely grooved into tiny sharp teeth; girdle naked, scaled like cancellate chitons, or matted with spines; ours, Florida to Texas.

Class Gastropoda (Univalves)

Diagnosis: typically asymmetrical; head well developed; flat, ventral foot present; shell undivided, typically external, some internal or absent; freshwater, marine, or land; mostly hermaphroditic, also biparental; development with or without a larval stage, land forms are typified by direct development, aquatic forms by larvae; feeding habits of all types, land and freshwater forms mostly herbivorous.

FRESHWATER GASTROPODS
Subclass Prosobranchiata (Operculate Snails)

Diagnosis: shell closed by a lid, or operculum; with internal gills.

Order Archaeogastropoda

Diagnosis: operculum semicircular, with a loose spiral, not notched.

Tongue Snails (Family Neretidae)—shell small, thin; columella (inner lip of aperture, the thickened axis of the shell) not toothed; rare, Alabama rivers only.

Toothed Snails (Family Neretidae)—shell large, thick; columella generally toothed; Gulf Coast and Florida, fresh and brackish, generally quiet, water.

Order Mesogastropoda

Diagnosis: operculum semicircular or circular, if semicircular and loosely spiraled, also notched.

Apple Snails (Family Ampullariidae)—shell very large (largest freshwater snails), globose; operculum semicircular, concentric; aperture elongate, angular; Florida and Georgia, generally on mud.

Giant Viviparous Snails (Family Viviparidae)—operculum concentric; shell longer than .6 inch, globose, whorls neither flattened nor beaded.

Conical Viviparous Snails (Family Viviparidae)—operculum concentric, at least near margin; shell longer than .6 inch, conical, whorls neither flattened nor beaded.

Beaded Snails (Family Viviparidae)—operculum concentric; shell longer than .6 inch, conical to globose, whorls flattened and beaded.

Columbian Snails (Family Pilidae)—operculum concentric; shell longer than .6 inch, discoidal.

Round-Mouthed Snails (Family Valvatidae)—operculum circular, multispiral; shell longer than .6 inch, generally globose.

Blunt River Snails (Family Pleuroceridae)—operculum spiral, not circular in outline; shell thick and heavy, more than .6 inch long, conical, blunt- or short-spired.

Knobbed River Snails (Family Pleuroceridae)—operculum spiral, not circular in outline; shell thick and heavy, more than .6 inch long, blunt- or short-spired, wall knobbed.

Rhomboidal River Snails (Family Pleuroceridae)—operculum spiral, not circular in outline; shell thick and heavy, more than .6 inch long, rhomboidal.

Slit River Snails (Family Pleuroceridae)—operculum spiral, not circular in outline; shell thick and heavy, more than .6 inch long, somewhat globose, aperture slit above.

Tower River Snails (Family Pleuroceridae)—operculum spiral, not circular in outline; shell thick and heavy, more than .6 inch long, elongate.

Oval River Snails (Family Pleuroceridae)—operculum spiral, not circular in outline; shell thick and heavy, more than .6 inch long, more-or-less oval.

False Viviparous Snails (Family Amnicolidae)—operculum concentric; shell less than .6 inch long, conical.

Tile Stream Snails (Family Amnicolidae)—operculum spi-

CHITONS

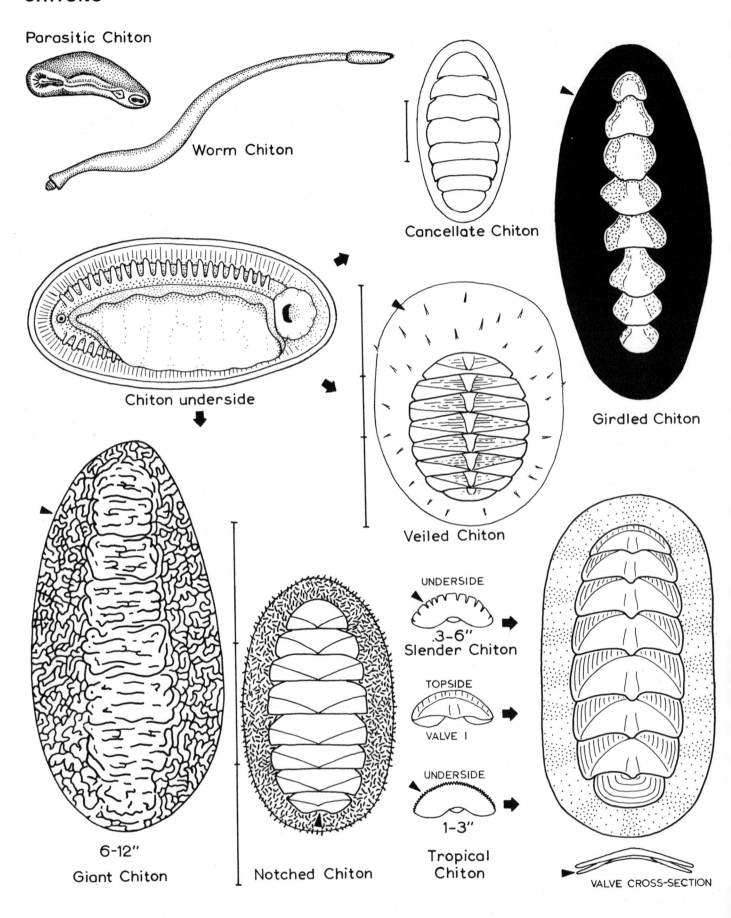

Parasitic Chiton

Worm Chiton

Cancellate Chiton

Girdled Chiton

Chiton underside

Veiled Chiton

6-12"
Giant Chiton

Notched Chiton

UNDERSIDE
.3-6"
Slender Chiton

TOPSIDE
VALVE I

UNDERSIDE
1-3"
Tropical Chiton

VALVE CROSS-SECTION

FRESH-WATER GASTROPODS

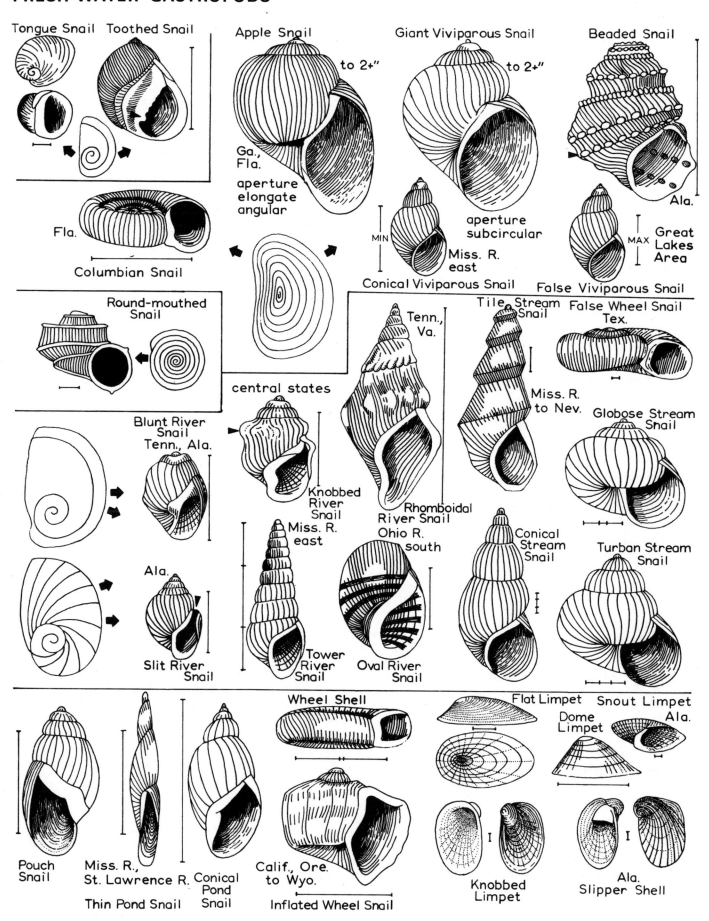

Tongue Snail   Toothed Snail

Fla.

Columbian Snail

Round-mouthed Snail

Apple Snail

to 2+"

Ga., Fla.

aperture elongate angular

Giant Viviparous Snail

to 2+"

aperture subcircular

MIN   Miss. R. east

Conical Viviparous Snail

Beaded Snail

Ala.

MAX   Great Lakes Area

False Viviparous Snail

central states

Tenn., Va.

Tile Stream Snail

Miss. R. to Nev.

False Wheel Snail Tex.

Globose Stream Snail

Knobbed River Snail

Rhomboidal River Snail

Blunt River Snail Tenn., Ala.

Ala.

Slit River Snail

Miss. R. east

Tower River Snail

Ohio R. south

Oval River Snail

Conical Stream Snail

Turban Stream Snail

Pouch Snail

Miss. R., St. Lawrence R.

Thin Pond Snail

Conical Pond Snail

Wheel Shell

Calif., Ore. to Wyo.

Inflated Wheel Snail

Flat Limpet

Dome Limpet

Knobbed Limpet

Snout Limpet Ala.

Ala. Slipper Shell

63

raled, not circular; shell less than .4 inch long, elongate, whorls tilelike.

False Wheel Snails (Family Amnicolidae)—operculum spiraled, not circular; shell less than .4 inch long, discoidal.

Globose Stream Snails (Family Amnicolidae)—operculum spiraled, not circular; shell less than .4 inch long, globose.

Conical Stream Snails (Family Amnicolidae)—operculum spiraled, not circular; shell less than .4 inch long, conical.

Turban Stream Snails (Family Amnicolidae)—operculum spiraled, not circular; shell less than .4 inch long, turbanlike.

SUBCLASS PULMONATA (Pulmonate or Lunged Snails)

Diagnosis: shell without an operculum; without gills; 1 freshwater order, Basommatophora.

Pouch or Left-Handed Snails (Family Physidae)—shell grows counterclockwise, all other freshwater pulmonates grow clockwise; mostly northern states.

Thin Pond Snails (Family Lymnaeidae)—shell spiraled, elongate, thin.

Conical Pond Snails (Family Lymnaeidae)—shell spiraled, conical.

Wheel Snails (Family Planorbidae)—shell spiraled, discoidal.

Inflated Wheel Snails (Family Planorbidae)—shell spiraled, with a low spire.

Flat Limpets (Family Ancylidae)—shell caplike, flat, with neither knob at apex nor shelf inside.

Dome Limpets (Family Ancylidae)—shell caplike, tall, with neither knob at apex nor shelf inside; western states.

Snout Limpets (Family Ancylidae)—shell minute, short-spired, inner lip broadly dilated.

Knobbed Limpets (Family Ancylidae)—shell minute, caplike with knob at apex but no shelf inside.

Slipper Shells (Family Ancylidae)—shell minute, caplike with spire at apex and shelf inside (mature animals only).

LAND GASTROPODS
Subclass Prosobranchiata (Operculate Snails)

Diagnosis: shell closed by a lid, or operculum; internal gills.

Order Archaeogastropoda

Diagnosis: shell wider than it is high; whorls smooth.
Globular Lid Snails (Family Helicinidae)—shell globular.

Order Mesogastropoda

Diagnosis: shell higher than it is wide; whorls generally vertically lined or ribbed.
Conical Lid Snails (Family Pomatiasidae)—at least .3 inch long, generally longer; whorls having many fine ribs.
Conical Lid Snails (Family Truncatellidae)—less than .3 inch long; ribs heavy or absent.

SUBCLASS PULMONATA (Pulmonate or Lunged Snails)

Diagnosis: shell without an operculum; without gills.

Order Basommatophora

Diagnosis: head with 1 pair of tentacles.
Two-Tentacle Snails (Family Carychiidae)—shell elongate; lip of aperture bent backward, aperture with a tooth, knob, or folded spot; southwestern United States to Newfoundland and Florida.

Order Systellommatophora

Diagnosis: head with 2 pairs of contractile tentacles.
Hooded Slugs (Family Veronicellidae)—shell absent; body oblong, back rounded and covered by the skinlike mantle; color grayish to brownish mottled with black and with a median whitish band; ours, Florida only.

Order Stylommatophora

Diagnosis: head with 2 pairs of tentacles, invert rather than contract.

Suborder Heterurethra

Diagnosis: shell elongate, aperture at least half as long as shell.
Amber Snails (Family Succineidae)—shell thin, often amber-colored; generally near water.

Suborder Orthurethra

Diagnosis: shell less than .4 inch long; shell pupa-shaped, globular or depressed and generally with the whorls lined or the lip bent backward, or spindle-shaped with the inner lip (columella) of the aperture twisted and the length .2–.4 inches long.

Glossy Snails (Family Cionellidae)—shell glossy, almost translucent, spindle-shaped.

Ribbed Dome Snails (Family Strobilopsidae)—shell usually domed and ribbed; aperture with 1 or more folds or plates.

Ribbed Globular Snails (Family Valloniidae)—shell depressed to globular, usually ribbed (always ribbed when globular); aperture smooth.

Cylindrical Pupa Snails (Family Pupillidae)—shell pupa-shaped, cylindrical; aperture without true teeth, a toothlike calus may be present.

Toothed Pupa Snails (Family Pupillidae)—shell pupa-shaped; aperture distinctly toothed.

Conical Pupa Shells (Family Pupillidae)—shell pupa-shaped, conical; aperture with 0–1 tooth.

Obese Pupa Shells (Family Pupillidae)—shell globose but not ribbed; light to dark reddish brown; aperture smooth.

Suborder Mesurethra

Diagnosis: shell .8 inch or longer, pupa-shaped.

LAND GASTROPODS

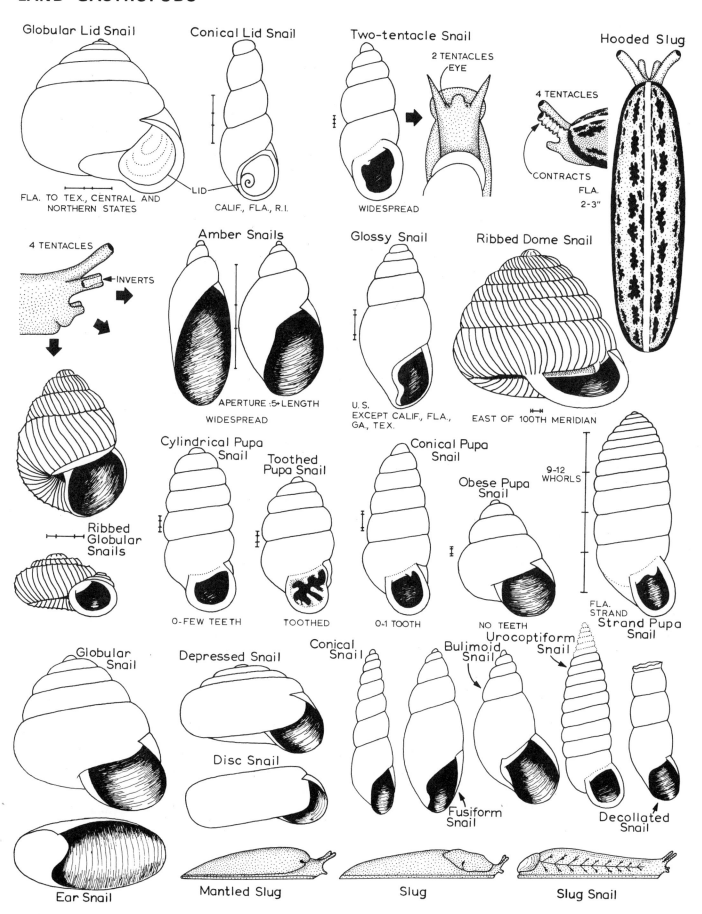

Globular Lid Snail

FLA. TO TEX., CENTRAL AND NORTHERN STATES

Conical Lid Snail

LID

CALIF., FLA., R.I.

Two-tentacle Snail

2 TENTACLES
EYE

WIDESPREAD

Hooded Slug

4 TENTACLES

CONTRACTS
FLA.
2-3"

4 TENTACLES

INVERTS

Amber Snails

APERTURE :5+ LENGTH

WIDESPREAD

Glossy Snail

U.S.
EXCEPT CALIF., FLA.,
GA., TEX.

Ribbed Dome Snail

EAST OF 100TH MERIDIAN

Ribbed
Globular
Snails

Cylindrical Pupa
Snail

0-FEW TEETH

Toothed
Pupa Snail

TOOTHED

Conical Pupa
Snail

0-1 TOOTH

Obese Pupa
Snail

NO TEETH

9-12
WHORLS

FLA.
STRAND

Strand Pupa
Snail

Globular
Snail

Depressed Snail

Disc Snail

Conical
Snail

Bulimoid
Snail

Urocoptiform
Snail

Fusiform
Snail

Decollated
Snail

Ear Snail

Mantled Slug

Slug

Slug Snail

Strand Pupa Snails (Family Cerionidae)—ours, Florida only, sea coast above high tide line.

Diagnosis: shell minute to large; not pupa-shaped, without ribs when globular, lip not bent backward when depressed, or columella straight (not twisted) when spindle-shaped (also less than .2 or greater than .4 inch long); figured types recognized according to shell form, generally not taxonomically meaningful.

MARINE GASTROPODS

Most of the species of the three subclasses of gastropods are found in the ocean. Because of the multitude of individuals in these subclasses, difficulties arise when attempt at systematic recognition of subclasses, orders, etc. is made. In addition, identification is based upon anatomy of soft parts rather than the shell, so it is not really practical to use characteristics of the shell, when present, to identify the various groups. In fact, no simple means can be used to separate the subclasses, for even the presence or absence of an operculum is not indicative of a single subclass.

These problems are bypassed in two ways here. First, for all practical purposes the treatment is limited to intertidal forms. Second, there is no discussion of individual types; features helpful in identification are limited to and stressed in the drawings. Especially useful in examining the figures are shape and sculpturing, the presence or absence of a pearly shell interior and notches in the shell aperture, and the nature of muscle scars and the interior lip of the aperture (especially shape and sculpture). Illustrated types fit into the following classification:

Subclass Prosobranchiata
  Order Archaeogastropoda
    Suborder Docoglossa—limpets
    Suborder Rhipidoglossa—abalones, slit shells, keyhole limpets, turban shells, top shells, pheasant shells, and arenes
  Order Mesogastropoda
    Suborder Pentoglossa—wentletraps and purple sea snails
    Suborder Taenioglossa—cup and saucer shells, Chinese hat shells, slipper shells, half slipper shells, hoof shells, pouch shells, worm shells, ear shells, chink shells, periwinkles, moon shells, sun dial shells, turret shells, horn shells, bittia, conches, frog shells, hairy tritons, and cowries.
    Suborder Heteropoda—heteropods
  Order Neogastropoda
    Suborder Stenoglossa—rice shells, olive shells, dog whelks, miter shells, and whelks.
    Suborder Toxoglossa—false miter shells, auger shells, tower shells, and cone shells.

Subclass Opisthobranchiata
  Order Tectibranchiata
    Suborder Cephalaspidea—paper bubble shells, baby bubble shells, barrel bubble shells, pyram shells, bubble shells, and lined sea slugs.
    Suborder Anaspidea—sea hares
    Suborder Notaspidea—shielded sea slugs
    Suborder Gymnosomata (Pteropoda)—sea butterflies
  Order Nudibranchiata—sea slugs
  Order Onchidiata—fringed sea slugs
Subclass Pulmonata
  Order Basommatophora—brackish water snails, marine snails, and false limpets

Class Pelecypoda (Bivalves)

Diagnosis: bilaterally symmetrical; body without a distinct head but with a mouth bounded by flaps (labial palps); foot often large, usually wedge-shaped; shell divided into 2 valves; mostly biparental, also hermaphroditic; egg to larva to adult, freshwater larvae are fish gill parasites; most use gills to filter microorganisms for food.

The following treatment is limited mostly to intertidal and freshwater forms, subtidal bivalves usually being ignored:

Order Protobranchia

Diagnosis: gills unique in gross form.
Awning Clams (Suborder Solemyacea)—shell with a skinlike fringe; hinge toothless.
Nut Clams (Suborder Nuculacea)—shell without a skinlike fringe; hinge with many teeth.

Order Filibranchia

Diagnosis: gills unique in gross form.
Arc Shells (Suborder Taxondonta)—hinge many-toothed.
Scallops (Suborder Anisomyaria)—valves winged at hinge; valves neither oblique in shape nor gaping.
Oysters (Suborder Anisomyaria)—growth lines and surface of valve irregular.
Jingle Shells (Suborder Anisomyaria)—1 valve with and 1 without a hole.
Winged Oyster (Suborder Anisomyaria)—valves winged at hinge, 1 wing greatly elongate.
Swimming Clams (Suborder Anisomyaria)—valves winged at hinge; shell oblique in outline, gaping.
Thorny Oyster (Suborder Anisomyaria)—thorny or spiny.
Mussels (Suborder Anisomyaria)—valves oval to elongate, with unequal muscle scars.

Order Eulamellibranchia

Diagnosis: gills unique in gross form.
Piddocks (Suborder Adapedonta)—valve with thin projection in-

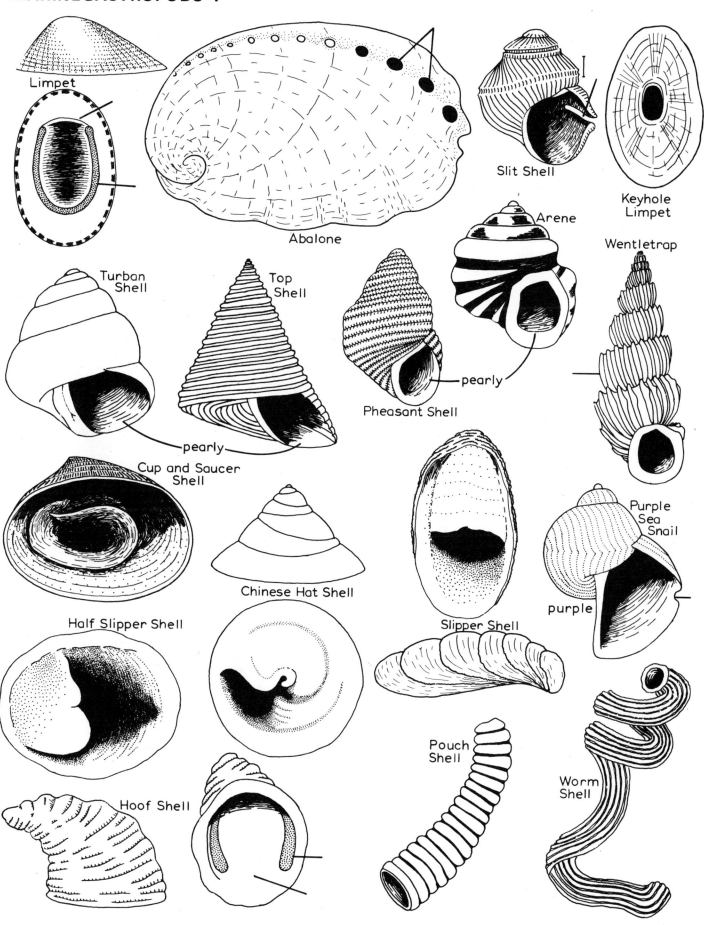

Limpet

Abalone

Slit Shell

Keyhole Limpet

Arene

Wentletrap

Turban Shell

Top Shell

Pheasant Shell

— pearly —

Purple Sea Snail

Cup and Saucer Shell

— pearly —

Half Slipper Shell

Chinese Hat Shell

Slipper Shell

purple

Hoof Shell

Pouch Shell

Worm Shell

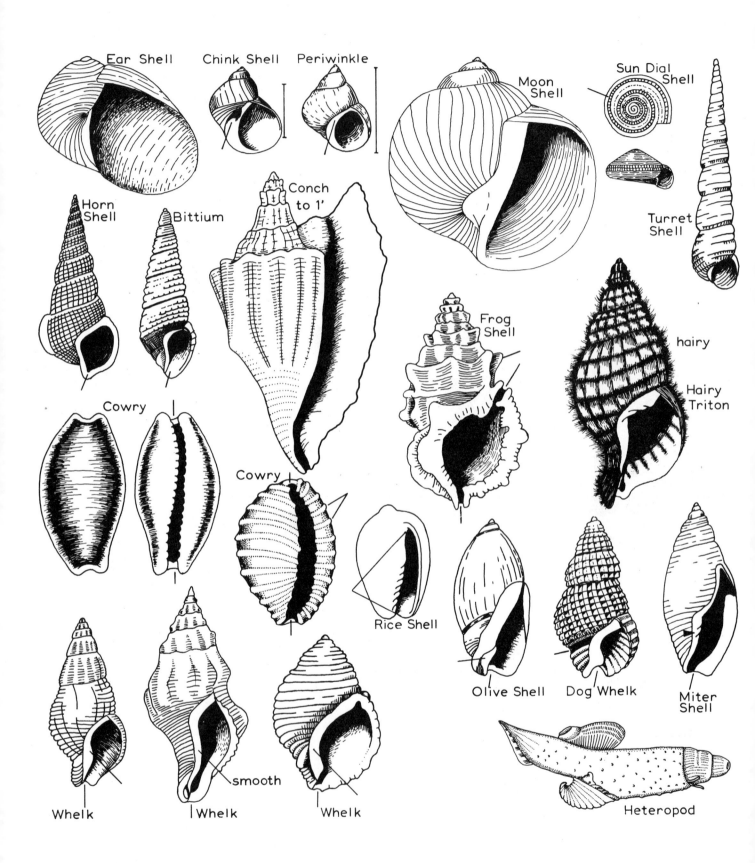

Ear Shell

Chink Shell

Periwinkle

Moon Shell

Sun Dial Shell

Horn Shell

Bittium

Conch to 1'

Turret Shell

Frog Shell

hairy

Hairy Triton

Cowry

Cowry

Rice Shell

Olive Shell

Dog Whelk

Miter Shell

Whelk

smooth Whelk

Whelk

Heteropod

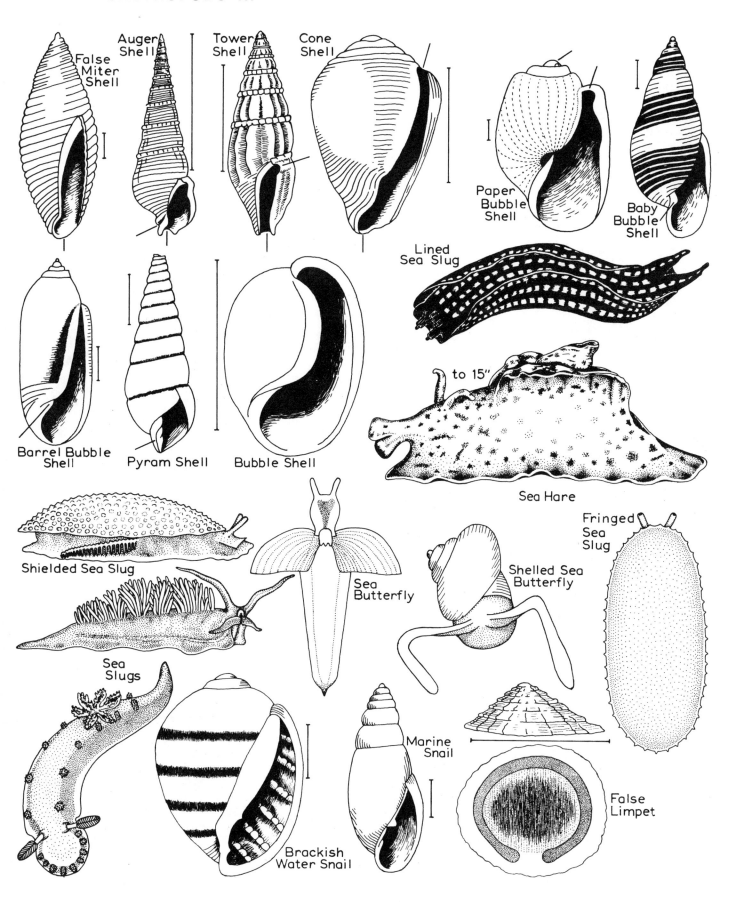

False
Miter
Shell

Auger
Shell

Tower
Shell

Cone
Shell

Paper
Bubble
Shell

Baby
Bubble
Shell

Lined
Sea Slug

Barrel Bubble
Shell

Pyram Shell

Bubble Shell

to 15"

Sea Hare

Shielded Sea Slug

Sea
Butterfly

Shelled Sea
Butterfly

Fringed
Sea
Slug

Sea
Slugs

Marine
Snail

Brackish
Water Snail

False
Limpet

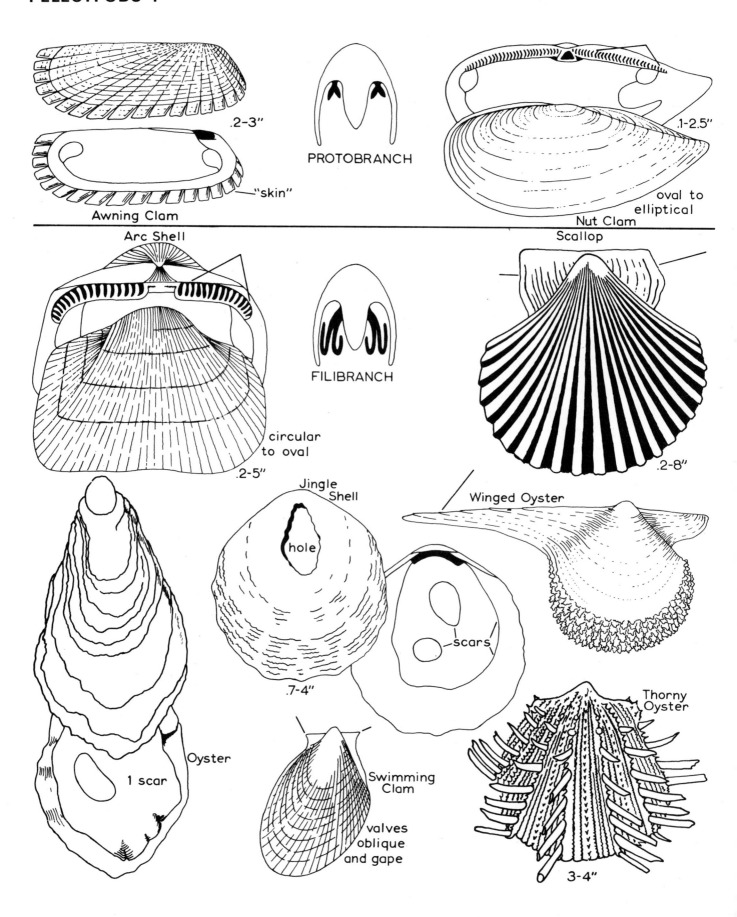

Awning Clam

.2-3"

"skin"

PROTOBRANCH

.1-2.5"

oval to elliptical

Nut Clam

Arc Shell

Scallop

FILIBRANCH

circular to oval

.2-5"

.2-8"

Jingle Shell

hole

Winged Oyster

.7-4"

scars

Oyster

1 scar

Swimming Clam

valves oblique and gape

Thorny Oyster

3-4"

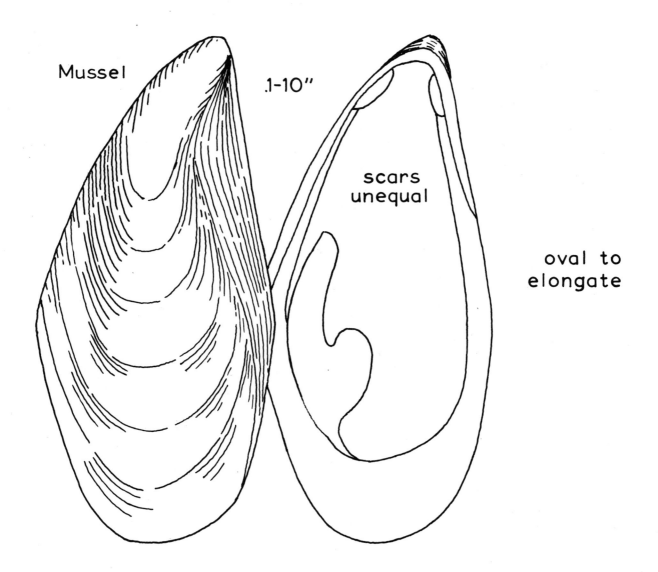

Mussel

.1-10"

scars
unequal

oval to
elongate

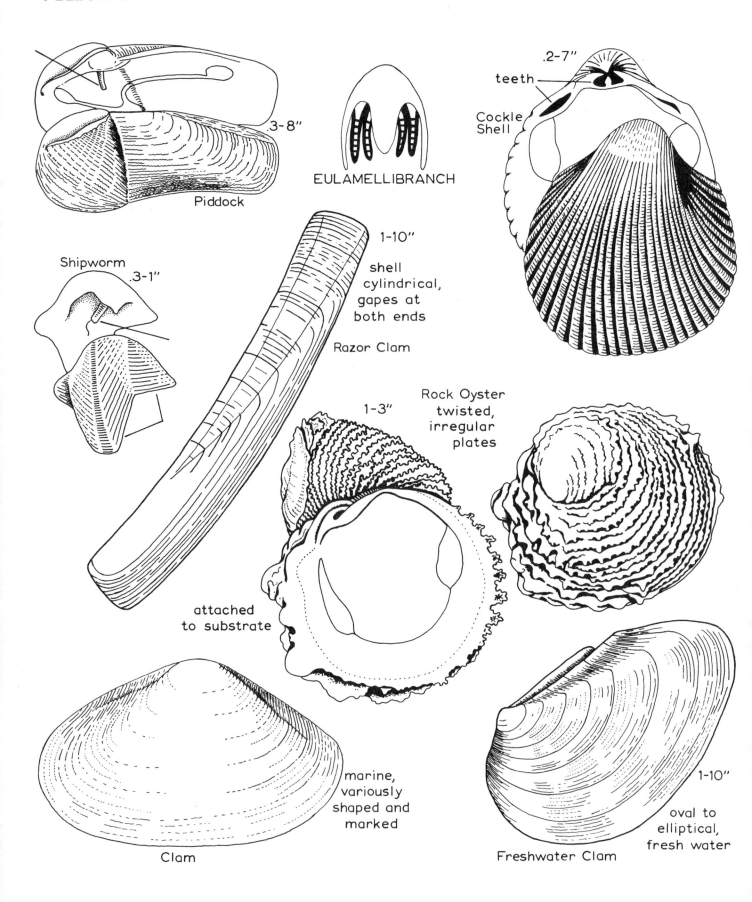

Piddock .3-8"

EULAMELLIBRANCH

.2-7"
teeth
Cockle Shell

Shipworm .3-1"

1-10"

shell cylindrical, gapes at both ends

Razor Clam

Rock Oyster twisted, irregular plates

1-3"

attached to substrate

marine, variously shaped and marked

Clam

1-10"

oval to elliptical, fresh water

Freshwater Clam

side and below hinge; valves not helmet-shaped, generally oval to elongate.

Shipworms (Suborder Adapedonta)—valve with thin projection inside and below hinge; valves helmet-shaped.

Razor Clams (Suborder Adapedonta)—shell elongate, inflated to cylindrical, gaping at both ends.

Cockle Shells (Suborder Heterodonta)—position of teeth unique; valves ribbed or essentially so.

Rock Oysters (Suborder Adapedonta)—valves unequal, twisted, with irregular plates; attached to hard substrates, generally rocks.

Clams (Suborder Heterodonta)—collective for other heterodonts, features not as in other eulamellibranchs.

Freshwater Clams (Suborder Schizodonta)—found only in fresh water.

Class Cephalopoda (Cephalopods)

Diagnosis: bilaterally symmetrical; body with a very well-developed head; foot modified into tentacles; siphon present and used for jet-propelled locomotion; shell undivided, conspicuous and external in nautili, reduced and internal or absent in squids and octupi; marine; mostly biparental, no larva, egg to adult; carnivorous, size of prey related to cephalopod size.

SUBCLASS TETRABRANCHIA

Diagnosis: includes about 5000 species of extinct ammonites and nautiloids, plus 3 living species of the genus *Nautilus*; *Nautilus* occurs in the Indo-Pacific, has many suckerless arms, 2 pairs of gills, and a large, external, chambered shell.

SUBCLASS DIBRANCHIA (Coleoidea)

Diagnosis: cephalopods with 8 or 10 arms that bear rows of suckers; shell internal or absent, external shell present only in female paper nautili.

Order Decapoda (Squid)

Diagnosis: body generally elongate, cylindrical; 10 arms, 2 longer than others; body and fin form help separate the various groups.

Spirulas (Family Spirulidae)—shell partly external, partly internal; subtidal Atlantic.

Bob-Tailed Squids (Family Sepiolidae)—body short, more-or-less globular, rounded at ends; fins rounded, separate, at sides near mid-body; subtidal.

Squids (Family Loliginidae)—body elongate, cylindrical, pointed at end; fins triangular to rounded, joined at end, outer margin not forming a right angle; subtidal.

Cuttlefishes (Family Sepiidae)—body short, oblong, somewhat pointed at end; fins narrow, joined at end, along length of body; subtidal Atlantic, probably not along North American shores.

Giant Squids (Family Architeuthidae)—largest known invertebrate; body somewhat elongate, round but swollen in middle, somewhat pointed at end; fins triangular, joined at end, apex of outer margin pointed toward head; deep sea.

Flying Squids or Sea Arrows (Family Ommastrephidae)—body generally streamlined, elongate, cylindrical and slender, pointed at end; fins usually triangular, joined at end, outer margin forming a sharp, more-or-less right angle; pelagic.

Lance-Tailed Squids (Family Galiteuthidae)—body elongate, cylindrical but rear portion very narrow, pointed at end; fins relatively narrow but long, lance-shaped; deep water.

Order Octopoda (Paper Nautili and Octopi)

Diagnosis: body generally short and stout; 8 arms, usually about the same length.

Paper Nautili (Family Argonautidae)—female to about 8 inches long, use broadly expanded dorsal arms to secrete and hold a delicate, thin, paperlike shell; males to about 1 inch long, without a shell; other octopi generally 2 inches or longer; pelagic, generally in warm waters.

Octopi (Family Octopodidae)—without a shell; head relatively large compared to body, fins absent; intertidal to deep sea.

Umbrella Octopi (Family Tremoctopodidae)—body relatively large, fins absent; 4 dorsal arms with long skin webs; 2 large holes in body in front of eyes; pelagic in warm waters.

Order Vampyromorpha ("Winged Octopi")

Diagnosis: mostly extinct, 1 living deep sea species; 10 arms but 2nd pair small and can be withdrawn into pockets at base of web uniting arms; octopuslike, body generally short and stout, relatively large; fins present.

ECHIUROIDEA (SPOONWORMS)

Diagnosis: wormlike, body unsegmented; gray, yellowish, or reddish worms; anterior snout usually well-developed and either spoonlike or threadlike; proboscis is contractile but cannot be withdrawn into the body; includes the innkeeper, a mudflat burrower that frequently has other animals as "tenants," mostly detritus feeders that trap materials on their outspread, mucous-covered snouts; the innkeeper forms a funnel (directed into its mouth) by exuding mucus as it backs farther into its burrow, then body movements are used to pump water through the funnel and burrow, when the sievelike funnel is full of food the worm consumes the funnel; biparental; egg to mobile larva to adult; in forked spoonworms the male

Cambrian Nautiloid (extinct)

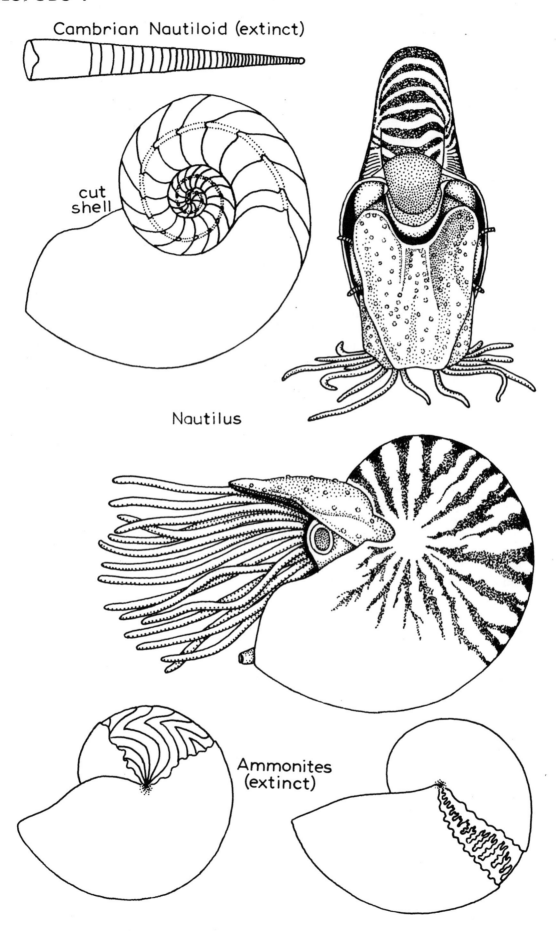

cut
shell

Nautilus

Ammonites
(extinct)

CEPHALOPODS II

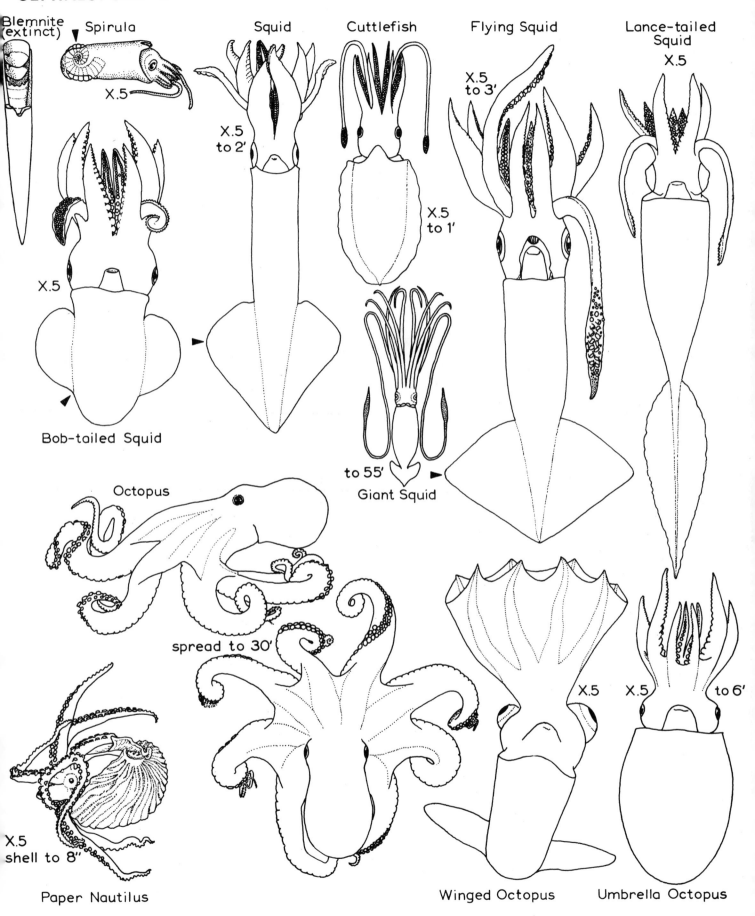

Blemnite (extinct)

Spirula
X.5

Squid
X.5 to 2'

Cuttlefish
X.5 to 1'

Flying Squid
X.5 to 3'

Lance-tailed Squid
X.5

Bob-tailed Squid
X.5

to 55'
Giant Squid

Octopus
spread to 30'

Winged Octopus
X.5

Umbrella Octopus
X.5   to 6'

Paper Nautilus
X.5 shell to 8"

SPOONWORMS

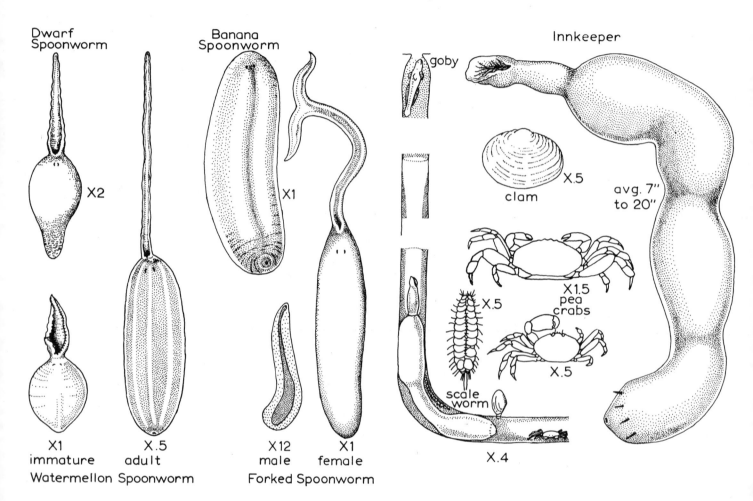

Dwarf
Spoonworm

X2

X1
immature
Watermellon Spoonworm

X.5
adult

Banana
Spoonworm

X1

X12
male

X1
female

Forked Spoonworm

goby

clam
X.5

X.4

scale
worm
X.5

X1.5
pea
crabs

X.5

Innkeeper

avg. 7"
to 20"

sex is determined by a larva contacting a female, males are parasites of females, larvae not contacting females become females.

Spoonworms resemble club and peanut worms but the nature of the spoonworm proboscis, or snout, is unique. *Habitat:* mostly marine burrowers in sand or mud; some live in rock or coral crevices, 1 off our southeast coast lives in the skeletal (test) remains of sand dollars.

ANNELIDA (SEGMENTED WORMS)

Diagnosis: wormlike, body segmented, composed of many essentially similar ringlike segments; resemble many worms but are the only common worms with segmentation.
Habitat: freshwater, marine, damp soil, and parasitic.

Class Polychaeta (Marine Segmented Worms)

Diagnosis: head distinct, marked by sensory structures, (eyes, tentacles and/or palps); usually with lateral, vaguely leaflike structures (parapodia) having many bristles (setae); regularly biparental, also hermaphroditic, egg to mobile larva to adult; marine except for a few freshwater forms, clamworms from the San Francisco and Salton Sea areas of California, tentacle worms from near Philadelphia, Lake Superior and Lake Erie.

No simple, completely taxonomic subdivision of the class is possible.

Archiannelids—segmentation generally poorly indicated externally; setae and parapodia absent or reduced.
Feather-Duster Worms—many feathery gills provide a "feather-duster;" live in tubes; plankton feeders.
Sea Mice—body oval, about 3 inches long, sides covered by iridescent, flexible bristles; plankton feeders.
Crested Worms—tentacles long; live in tubes; detritus feeders.
Tentacle Worms—tentacles short; live in tubes; detritus feeders.
Bamboo Worms—body segmentation vaguely reminiscent of bamboo; live in tubes; detritus feeders.
Fragile Worms—body elongate, fragile, typified by 1st and last segments; burrow in sand; detritus feeders.
Gold Crown Worms—mouth with gold-colored bristles; live in tubes; detritus feeders.
Bristle-Headed Worms—head bearing typical bristles; mostly under tidepool rocks; detritus feeders.
Shield Worms—body shape distinctive, posterior end bearing a shield and appendages; live in burrows; detritus feeders.
Scale Worms—top of body covered by distinctive scales; live in cracks, in crevices, and among objects; predators.

Lugworms—vaguely resemble earthworms but have a bulblike process on the front end and no collar; burrowers, usually in sand or mud; detritus feeders.
Clamworms—body elongate, with prominent lateral appendages; found hidden in cracks and among objects, also in open; predators.
Fan Worms—head and certain enlarged appendages on the sides of the body are distinctive; live in U-shaped burrows in sand or mud; detritus feeders.
Proboscis Worms—with a long eversible proboscis, otherwise resemble clamworms; burrowers, usually in sand or mud; predators.
Glass Worms—shape unique; pelagic; predators.

Class Oligochaeta (Earthworms, Bristleworms and Allies)

Diagnosis: head indistinct, not marked by sensory structures; without parapodia; setae present but few in number; hermaphroditic, development direct, egg to adult (eggs often in cocoons); in moist soil or fresh water except for some rare bristleworms and earthworms.
Oil Droplet Worms (Family Aelosomatidae)—with neither collar nor suckers; body generally with bristles, containing colorless or colored oil droplets; to .4 inch long; mostly detritus feeders; freshwater in mud or debris.
Bristleworms (many families)—with neither collar nor suckers; body generally with bristles, without oil droplets; usually under 1.2 inches long; mostly detritus feeders; generally freshwater in mud or debris, in or out of tubes.
Crayfish Worms (Family Branchiobdellidae)—leechlike but with caudal and without oral sucker; without bristles; to about .4 inch long; probably strictly commensals, limited to living on crayfishes.
Earthworms (many families)—segments about 1/3 back on body modified, united into a collar; without suckers; bristles reduced; mostly in moist soil, infrequent in fresh water, very rarely marine.

Class Hirudinea (Leeches)

Diagnosis: head indistinct, site indicated only by a sucker; without parapodia or setae; hermaphroditic, development direct, egg to adult; mostly in fresh water, some live on marine fishes and some in moist places on land; parasites (feeding mostly on blood of crustaceans and vertebrates), scavengers (mostly on animal remains), and predators (mostly on small worms, insects and mollusks).

ARTHROPODA (JOINT-LEGGED ANIMALS)

Diagnosis: in most, body segmented, visible externally in various degrees, usually covered by a hard, external skele-

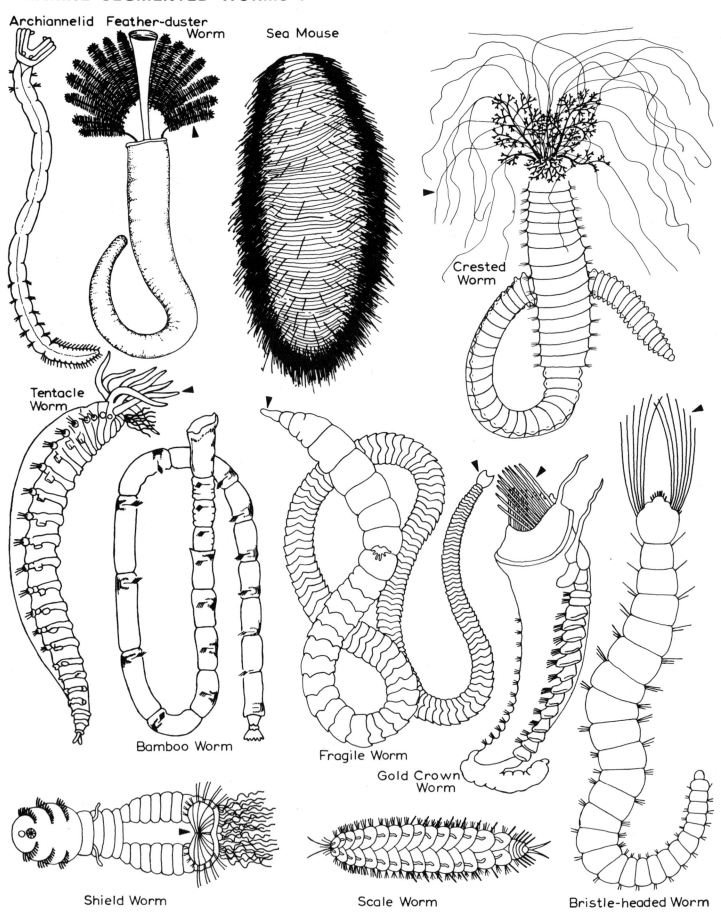

Archiannelid   Feather-duster Worm   Sea Mouse

Crested Worm

Tentacle Worm

Bamboo Worm

Fragile Worm

Gold Crown Worm

Shield Worm

Scale Worm

Bristle-headed Worm

MARINE SEGMENTED WORMS II-OLIGOCHAETS-LEECHES

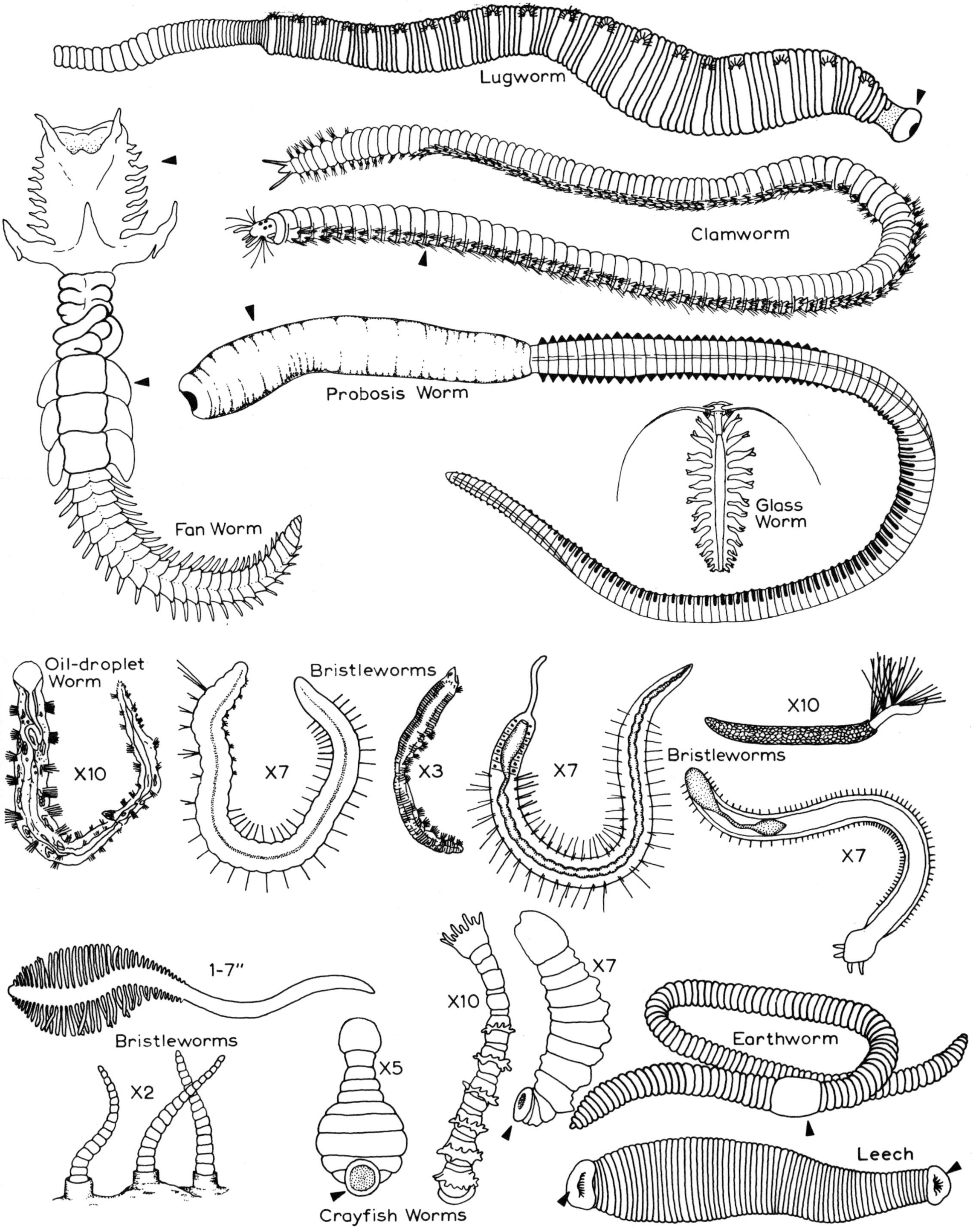
Lugworm
Clamworm
Fan Worm
Probosis Worm
Glass Worm
Oil-droplet Worm
X10
Bristleworms
X7
X3
X7
Bristleworms
X10
X7
1-7"
Bristleworms
X2
X5
X10
X7
Crayfish Worms
Earthworm
Leech

ton; appendages when present are jointed; tongue worms are wormlike, unsegmented parasites but their bodies are constricted into rings that appear to be segments; without appendages but there are 2 pairs of hooks, a pair on either side of the mouth; other wormlike forms have stubby legs; contain more species and individuals than all other phyla combined.

Habitat: marine, freshwater, land, air (many insects), and parasitic.

SUBPHYLUM ONYCHOPHORA (Joint-legged Worms)

Diagnosis: found in West Indies, Mexico, Central America, and Southern Hemisphere; about 70 species of interest because of their "missing-link" features between Annelida and Arthropoda; vaguely caterpillarlike, a head with a pair of eyes, two "feelers" (antennae), and mouth bounded on each side by a blunt projection (oral papilla), without a shell; resemble annelids in having the same kind of excretory organs (nephridia); body externally unsegmented, with poorly developed, barely jointed legs; respiration by air tubes (tracheae) as in many land arthropods; mostly under objects in moist tropical forests or along streams; inactive in retreats during cold or dry periods; biparental, the young being born alive.

SUBPHYLUM PENTASTOMIDA (Linguatulida) (Tongue Worms)

Diagnosis: wormlike, unsegmented parasites, but body constricted into rings that appear to be segments; cephalothorax (joined head plus thorax) short, without appendages except for 2 pairs of ventral hooks on either side of the mouth; arthropod-like in body covering (chitinous cuticle), muscles, and nerve cord; without jointed legs or circulatory, respiratory, and excretory organs; vertebrate respiratory parasites; biparental, some with complex life histories with larval stages involving a change of animal hosts.

SUBPHYLUM TARDIGRADA (Water Bears)

Diagnosis: wormlike, unsegmented, but with 4 pairs of short, thick, unjointed legs terminated by claws, last pair of legs at end of body; without antennae, circulatory or respiratory organs; body covered by a cuticle that lacks chitin (a material distinctive for arthropods); microscopic to 1/25 inch long; freshwater, marine, and damp soil; can survive long periods in a shriveled, dried, apparently lifeless state; biparental, eggs laid or shed with molting of old cuticle, larval stages generally present but normally resemble adults in appearance.

SUBPHYLUM TRILOBITA (Trilobites)

Diagnosis: all extinct, Cambrian to Permian; hardly like any living creatures, perhaps vaguely sowbuglike; body covered by a shell and divided by 2 lengthwise dorsal furrows into 3 lobes; head, thorax and abdomen distinct; body could be rolled up as in certain pillbugs; head with one pair of antennae and 2 eyes; appendages simple; marine; biparental with larval stages.

SUBPHYLUM CHELICERATA (Chelicerates)

Diagnosis: body usually of 2 parts, cephalothorax (head + thorax) and abdomen, in Acarina (mites and ticks) cephalothorax and abdomen are fused together; cephalothorax has 1st pair of appendages with claws (chelicerae), one pair of projecting appendages (pedipalps), and 4 pairs of thoracic legs, but no antennae; cephalothorax and abdomen typically without obvious external segmentation.

Class Merostomata (Merostomates)

Diagnosis: 2 lateral eyes, each composed of many individual perception units grouped into a compound eye; body covered by a shell (including an extensive, solid, anterior portion, the carapace), abdominal appendages bearing specialized respiratory structures (gills), abdomen terminated by an elongate, daggerlike structure; only Chelicerata with abdominal legs, 5 or 6 pairs; marine.

SUBCLASS EURYPTERIDA (Sea Scorpions)

Diagnosis: all extinct, Ordovidian to Pennsylvanian; only vaguely scorpionlike, mostly small marine predators, but one to 7 feet long, the largest known fossil arthropod; external skeleton (carapace) covering cephalothorax but not expanded.

SUBCLASS XIPHOSURA (Horseshoe Crabs)

Diagnosis: mostly extinct, Cambrian to Recent; about 5 species of the genus *Limulus* now living (inhabit the Atlantic Coast from Maine to Florida, the West Indies, and the eastern shores of Asia; cephalothorax covered by an arched, expanded carapace of horseshoe outline; to 20 inches long, ours on sand or mud, 2–6 fathoms, generally burrow along surface, shell may be exposed, feed on various marine worms.

Class Pycnogonida (Sea Spiders)

Diagnosis: mostly minute, but to about 20 inches; vaguely spiderlike; 4 simple eyes; usually 8 walking legs

ARTHROPODS I

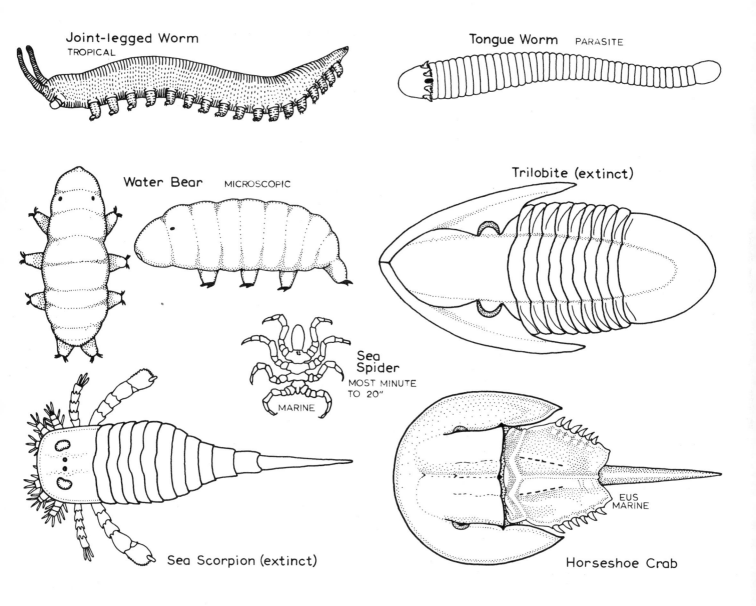

Joint-legged Worm TROPICAL

Tongue Worm PARASITE

Water Bear MICROSCOPIC

Trilobite (extinct)

Sea Spider MOST MINUTE TO 20" MARINE

Sea Scorpion (extinct)

Horseshoe Crab EUS MARINE

(also 10 or 12); without excretory or respiratory systems; often on seaweeds or animals.

Class Arachnida (Arachnids)

Diagnosis: eyes all simple; pedipalpi mostly sensory, but male's often modified for sperm transfer; without gills; mostly biparental, development regularly direct but a larval stage is present in mites and ticks; predominantly terrestrial and arthropod predators.

Order Scorpionida (Scorpions)

Diagnosis: pincers present; abdomen with a tail-like part ending in a stinger; terrestrial, generally in warm, dry regions where they are active at night, preying upon insects, spiders, and other scorpions; hide in burrows or under ground objects during the day; poisonous but only 2 of ours, Arizona species, are considered truly dangerous to man; females bear living young which stay a week or more on their mother's back.

Order Pseudoscorpionida (Pseudoscorpions)

Diagnosis: pincers present; abdomen without a tail-like part or stinger; terrestrial, found under ground objects, under bark, in cracks and crevices, in human dwellings, in caves, and in bee, termite, or ant nests; some along beaches, a few even intertidal; poison glands associated with pincers, but too small to bite man; noted for habit of attaching to and being transported by flying insects.

Order Acarina (Acari) (Mites and Ticks)

Diagnosis: body oval, cephalothorax broadly joined to abdomen; most without visible segmentation; mostly minute reddish creatures; terrestrial on plants and animals, in soil, and in stored foods; freshwater, marine, and plant and animal parasites; the Rocky Mountain spotted fever tick transmits a disease that often proves fatal to man; larvae with 3 pairs, adults with normal 4 pairs of legs.

Harvestman Mites (Suborder Notostigmata)—harvestmenlike; legs elongate; body segmented; bright blue-, gold-, and violet-colored; free-living.

Gall Mites (Suborder Tetrapodilidae)—somewhat wormlike; body segmented; 2 pairs of legs; parasitic on plants, most forming galls.

Follicle Mites (Suborder Thrombidiformes)—body elongate; parasitic on mammal hair glands.

Itch Mites (Suborder Thrombidiformes)—legs distinctive; in mammal skin.

Soft Ticks (Suborder Parasitiformes)—large; without a hard shell in the head region; external parasites of reptiles, birds, and mammals.

Hard Ticks (Suborder Parasitiformes)—large; with a hard shell in the head region; external parasites of reptiles, birds, and mammals.

Red Spider Mites (Suborder Thrombidiformes)—form distinctive; barely visible as red, orange, or yellow specks on leaves; plant parasites.

Chiggers (Suborder Thrombidiformes)—form distinctive; larval stages occur in skin of mammals.

Water Mites (Suborder Thrombidiformes)—the only aquatic mites; mostly red, also orange.

Order Phalangida (Opiliones) (Harvestmen or Daddy Longlegs)

Diagnosis: somewhat spiderlike; body short and oval, without distinct separation of head, thorax, and abdomen; abdomen segmented; legs extremely long and slender; body small but legs up to 6 inches long; terrestrial, in the open and under objects in fields, woods, or about human habitations; primarily scavengers, also prey on small insects and suck plant juices.

Order Solpugida (Solifugae) (Wind Scorpions or Sun Spiders)

Diagnosis: elongate and somewhat spiderlike but abdomen consists of 10 segments and is broadly joined to caphalothorax, also lack spinning organs and chelicerae with a terminal fang; chelicerae (not pedpialpi) are modified into pincers; pedipalpi long and leglike, but are sensory and held forward like antennae; largest pincers for their size of any arachnid; mostly night predators of dry lands, under objects or in burrows during the day; voracious predators on arthropods, known to kill small vertebrates.

Order Palpigrada (Microwhip Scorpions)

Diagnosis: resemble whip scorpions, but pedipalps are leglike and eyes are lacking; minute; often with bristle-tails; terrestrial, generally under objects, in ground, and in caves; occur in temperate and tropical areas, ours in Texas and California.

Order Pedipalpida (Uropygi) (Whip Scorpions)

Diagnosis: scorpionlike, but abdomen terminated by a whiplike structure rather than a tail and stinger; terrestrial, generally in dry regions, ours coast-to-coast across southern United States; nocturnal predators, under objects during the day; when irritated, elevate abdomen and release secretion with vinegarlike odor, called "vinegaroons."

Order Amblypygi (Whip Spiders)

Diagnosis: spiderlike, but 2nd pair of legs very long and whiplike; terrestrial, generally in dry regions; tropical and semitropical including southern and southwestern

United States; nocturnal predators, under objects during the day, also in caves.

Order Ricinuleida (Ricinuleids)

Diagnosis: one of the rarest groups of animals; spider-like, but without fangs (chelicerae antennaelike); ours known only from the Rio Grande River region from under long undisturbed, damp, house construction materials; also known from caves in Mexico.

Order Araneae (Araneida) (Spiders)

Diagnosis: cephalothorax and abdomen narrowly joined ("waist"), both unsegmented; chelicerae with a poison duct in claw; posterior abdomen with silk-spinning organs (spinnerets); poisonous but few are dangerous to man; mostly terrestrial, a few freshwater and marine; predators, 2nd to insects as greatest predators on insects; webs typify many groups.

Suborder Mygalomorphae (Orthognatha) (Tarantulas)

Diagnosis: fangs directed backward.

Purse Web Spiders (Family Atypidae)—abdomen with 1 or more hard scales; thoracic groove a transverse pit; east of Mississippi River, rare except in hummocks of Florida and Georgia; dig holes a foot or more deep, usually next to trees, a silken tube ("purse") lines hole and extends to about 1/2 foot above ground.

Folding-Door Tarantulas (Family Antrodiaetidae)—abdomen with 1 or more hard scales; thoracic groove longitudinal; last segment of posterior spinnerets as long as the previous segment; dig holes, partly to completely lined with silk, either leave hole open, elevate hole into a turret which at times is closed with silk or debris, or close hole with 2, equal, semicircular, folding doors that close in a straight line at the center of the hole; generally in thickets or along shaded streams, mostly California to Florida, Pacific Northwest, and Mountain States.

Sheet Web Tarantulas (Family Mecicobothriidae)—abdomen with 1 or more hard scales; thoracic groove longitudinal; last segment of posterior spinnerets as long as the previous 2 segments; occur in wooded areas under leaves, wood, and other debris, form loose, silk sheets in a single plane; webs resemble those of sheet web weavers; these spiders also resemble sheet web weavers); Pacific States.

Tarantulas (Family Theraphosidae)—abdomen without scales; feet with 2 claws and claw tufts; thoracic groove transverse to elliptical; generally in open areas, dig burrows or occupy rodent burrows or suitable natural cracks and crevices, usually have loose web over entrance when inside hole, hunt within a few feet of retreat; mostly southwest, Missouri and Arkansas to California.

Trapdoor Spiders (Family Ctenizidae)—abdomen without scales; feet with 3 claws, without claw tufts; thoracic groove transverse; head higher than thorax; dig simple or branched holes, coat with earth-saliva mixture, partly to completely line with silk, usually close holes with a thin to thick, single or double (like folding-door tarantulas') flap or trapdoor; occur mainly along line of southern-most states, California to Florida.

Funnel Web Tarantulas (Family Dipluridae)—abdomen without scales; feet with 3 claws, without claw tufts; thoracic groove circular; head not higher than thorax; form a sheetlike web with a funnel that extends into a crack or crevice, into dense plant growth, or under a rock; generally in dense vegetation, often woodlands or forests; Washington and Idaho south to California and Texas plus mountains of North Carolina and Tennesee.

Suborder Araneomorphae (Labidognatha) (True Spiders)

Diagnosis: fangs directed towards mid-body or essentially so, not distinctly backward.

Hackled-Band Weavers (Superfamily Dictynoidea)—with a scalelike plate in front of spinnerets; high magnification discloses silk to be ribbonlike (composed of longitudinal and sheetlike threads) rather than threadlike, webs mostly irregular snares and orbs or part of orbs (resembling those of orb weavers).

Hunting Spiders (Superfamily Plecturoidea)—*either* with chelicerae fused at the base and with a process forming a pincer with the fang, *or* with 6 eyes; hunters having no true webs, build simple, generally flat and oval or tubular, retreats in cracks and under objects.

Jumping Spiders (Families Salticidae and Lyssomanidae)—2 claws on last segment of each foot; 3 or 4 rows of eyes, the front median 2 eyes much the largest; pursue or jump upon prey, make simple retreats but no webs.

Crab Spiders (Families Sparassidae and Thomisidae)—2 claws on each foot; 2 rows of eyes; forelegs twisted backwards, crablike; hunters that often ambush their prey, often live on plants, especially flowers, to ambush bees, wasps, etc.; weave neither webs nor retreats.

Running Spiders (Superfamily Clubionoidea, part)—2 claws on each foot; 2 rows of eyes; legs normal; hunters that generally form tubular retreats but no webs.

Dwarf Sheet Web Spiders (Family Hahnidae)—3 claws on each foot; 6 spinnerets forming a more-or-less transverse row; webs delicate, sheetlike, usually above but near ground and near water.

Funnel Web Spiders (Family Agelenidae)—3 claws on each foot; last joint of legs with a row of fine hairs that extend out at right angles from the leg surface; 1st joint of leg not notched; form sheetlike webs with a funnel-like part near one edge, funnel generally going to a retreat (crack, plant, etc.)

Lynx Spiders (Family Oxyopidae)—3 claws on each foot; last joint of leg with a row of fine hairs that extend out at right angles from the leg surface; 1st joint of hind legs

ARACHNIDS I

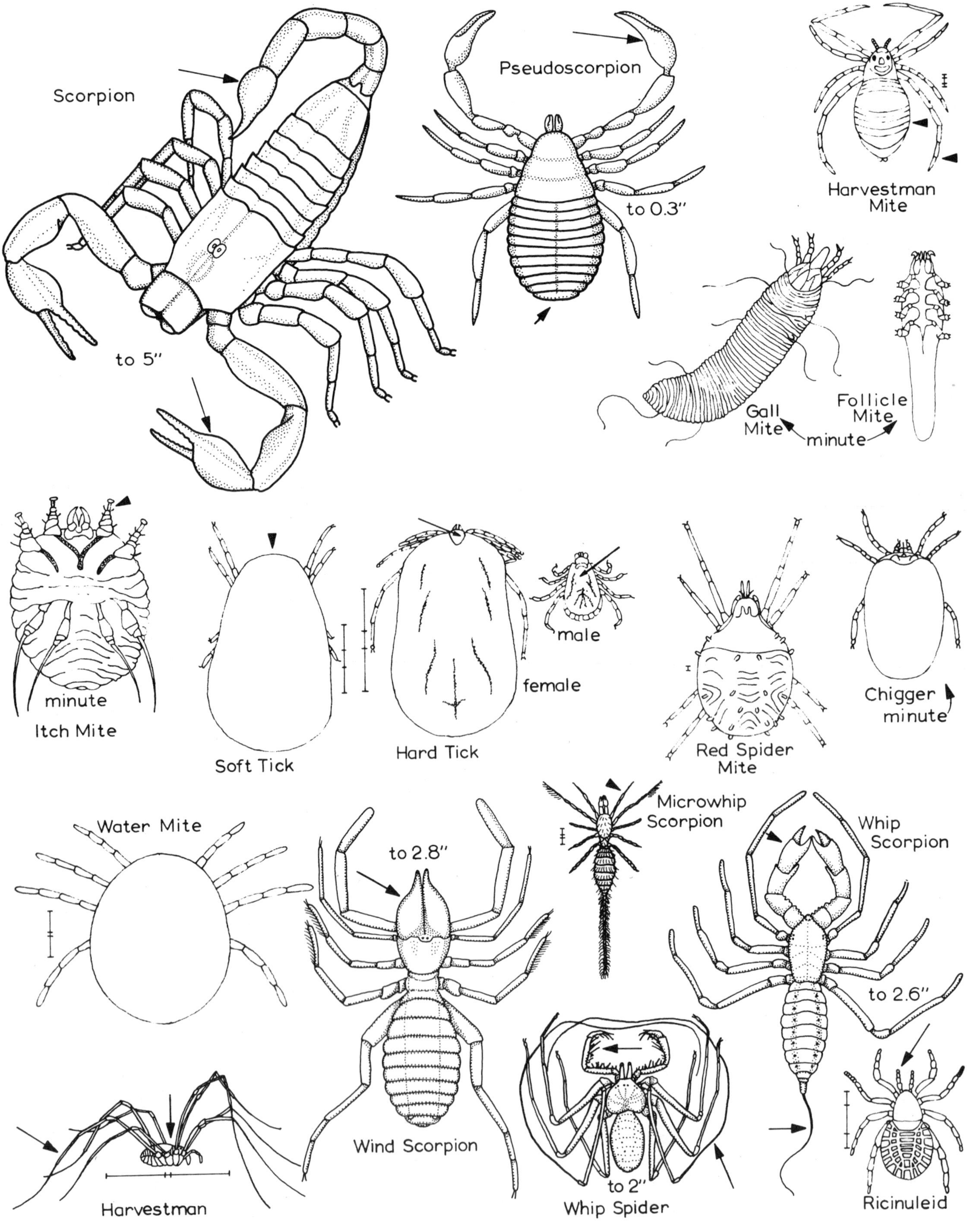
Scorpion
to 5"
Pseudoscorpion
to 0.3"
Harvestman Mite
Gall Mite
minute
Follicle Mite
Itch Mite
minute
Soft Tick
Hard Tick
male
female
Red Spider Mite
Chigger
minute
Water Mite
Wind Scorpion
to 2.8"
Microwhip Scorpion
Whip Scorpion
to 2.6"
Harvestman
to 2"
Whip Spider
Ricinuleid

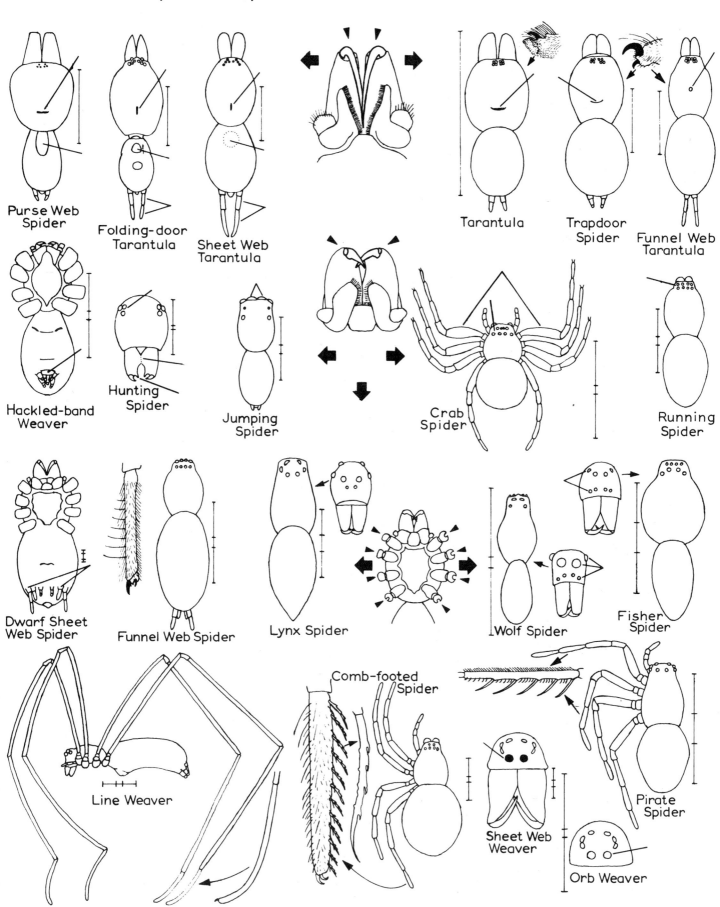

Purse Web Spider

Folding-door Tarantula

Sheet Web Tarantula

Tarantula

Trapdoor Spider

Funnel Web Tarantula

Hackled-band Weaver

Hunting Spider

Jumping Spider

Crab Spider

Running Spider

Dwarf Sheet Web Spider

Funnel Web Spider

Lynx Spider

Wolf Spider

Fisher Spider

Line Weaver

Comb-footed Spider

Sheet Web Weaver

Orb Weaver

Pirate Spider

notched; eye group hexagonal; live on shrubs or herbs, do not weave webs or retreats.

Wolf Spiders (Family Lycosidae)—3 claws on each foot; last joint of legs with a row of fine hairs that extend out at right angles from the leg; 1st joint of all legs notched; eyes in 3 rows; often encountered in the open, also under objects; do not weave webs, may weave retreats.

Fisher Spiders (Family Pisauridae)—3 claws on each foot; last joint of legs with a row of fine hairs that extend out at right angles from the leg surface; 1st joint of all legs notched; eyes in 2 rows; weave neither webs nor retreats; hunters, many near, upon, or under water.

Line Weavers (Family Pholcidae)—3 claws on each foot; last joint of legs very long, flexible, with false segments; webs sheetlike or irregular, spider hanging upside down from below, in dark places, especially cellars.

Comb-Footed Spiders (Family Theridiidae)—3 claws on each foot; last joint of hind legs with spines grouped into a comblike structure; webs irregular, spider often hanging upside down from below; includes dangerous black and less dangerous gray widows.

Pirate Spiders (Family Mimetidae)—3 claws on each foot; 2 joints next to last joint of the 1st and 2nd legs with long spines; hunters, especially on spiders, do not build webs.

Sheet Web Weavers (Family Linyphidae)—3 claws on each foot; eyes in a circle, the front 2 dark; web sheetlike, may be pulled into a dome, web often with an irregular part.

Orb Weavers (Superfamily Argiopoidea, part)—3 claws on each foot; eyes in a circle, all light-colored; build all or part of an orb web (consists of lines radiating in a single plane from the center plus attached sticky, trapping silk spiraling from the center), variously modified by lacking parts, being pulled into domes, having traplines, irregular components, etc.

SUBPHYLUM MANDIBULATA (Antennata)

Diagnosis: body consists of head plus trunk or plus thorax and abdomen; head with 1 or 2 pairs of antennae (first 2 appendage pairs), 1 pair of mandibles (jaws, the 3rd pair of appendages), 1 or more maxillae pairs, and 3 or more pairs of walking legs; sexes usually separate; eggs are laid or kept by the female until hatching; larval stages typically present.

Class Crustacea (Crustaceans)

Diagnosis: head with 2 pairs of antennae and 2 pairs of maxillae; body typically with a shell; shell usually with a single, extensive anterior portion, the carapace; exoskeleton, or shell, hard as a result of calcareous deposits; appendages often with 2, sometimes pincerlike, terminal segments, modified for walking, swimming, capturing food, respiration, and/or reproduction; sexes usually separate, eggs mostly carried by female, development typically with larval stages; mostly aquatic, also terrestrial and parasitic.

SUBCLASS CEPHALOCARIDA (Horseshoe Shrimp)

Diagnosis: neither eyes nor carapace present; head horseshoe-shaped; marine, very rare, in bays of Atlantic Coast and San Francisco, in mud.

SUBCLASS BRANCHIOPODA (Branchiopods)

Diagnosis: eyes present; carapace present or absent; thoracic appendages leaflike, 4 or more pairs, and with marginal gills; free-living, mostly in fresh water, filter feeders on microorganisms.

Order Anostraca (Fairy and Brine Shrimps)

Diagnosis: eyes stalked; carapace absent; includes brine shrimps of saline water and fairy shrimps of fresh water.

Order Notostraca (Tadpole Shrimps)

Diagnosis: eyes sessile; carapace a broad and low oval shield, resembling horseshoe crabs; tail with terminal, jointed, forked, whiplike appendages.

Order Conchostraca (Clam or Claw Shrimps)

Diagnosis: eyes sessile; carapace bivalved, clamlike, enclosing the compressed body; tail often with terminal claws.

Order Cladocera (Water Fleas)

Diagnosis: eyes sessile; carapace usually bivalved, somewhat clamlike, but never encloses head; tail often with terminal claws.

SUBCLASS OSTRACODA (Mussel or Seed Shrimps)

Diagnosis: eyes and carapace present, carapace bivalved, clamlike; resemble clam shrimps but have no more than 3 pairs of true thoracic appendages and these are not leaflike; free-living, aquatic, mostly bottom forms, filter feeders on microorganisms.

SUBCLASS MYSTACOCARIDA (Mustache Shrimps)

Diagnosis: 4 eyespots and carapace; antennules and antennae long; 4 pairs of simple thoracic segments; marine, intertidal sand, rare, known from South America, southern Africa, Mediterranean Sea, and Long Island Sound; filter feeders.

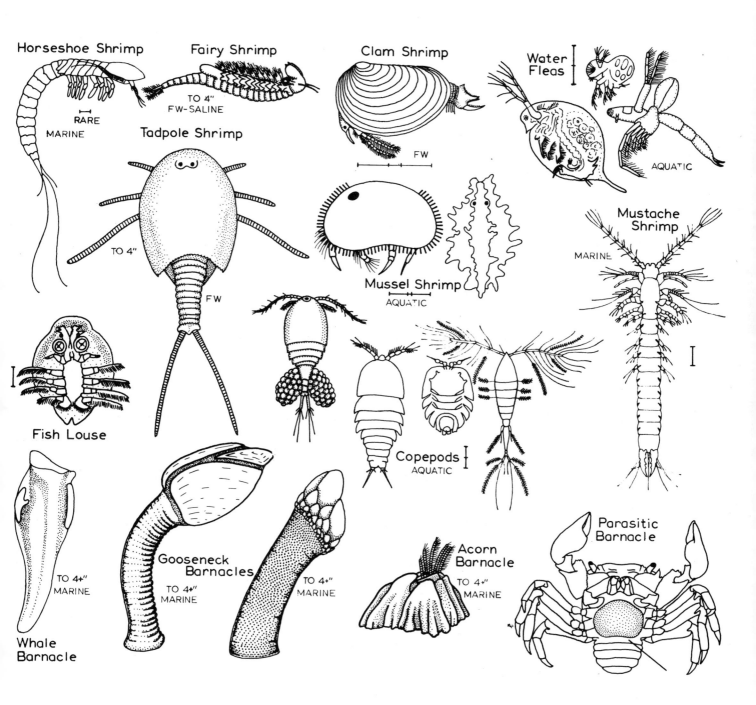

Horseshoe Shrimp
RARE
MARINE

Fairy Shrimp
TO 4"
FW-SALINE

Clam Shrimp
FW

Water Fleas
AQUATIC

Tadpole Shrimp
TO 4"
FW

Mussel Shrimp
AQUATIC

Mustache Shrimp
MARINE

Fish Louse

Copepods
AQUATIC

Whale Barnacle
TO 4+"
MARINE

Gooseneck Barnacles
TO 4+"
MARINE
TO 4+"
MARINE

Acorn Barnacle
TO 4+"
MARINE

Parasitic Barnacle

SUBCLASS BRANCHIURA (Fish Lice)

Diagnosis: compound eyes; carapace circular, large, covering head and thorax; body flat; parasitic on fresh- and saltwater fishes.

SUBCLASS COPEPODA (Copepods)

Diagnosis: typically 3 simple eyes fused into a single medial eye; carapace absent; typically 6 pairs of thoracic limbs, not leaflike, fewer or none in parasites; freshwater and marine, free-living filter feeders or parasitic, mostly on fish.

SUBCLASS CIRRIPEDIA (Barnacles)

Diagnosis: adults attached or parasitic; carapace of attached species becomes part of the body enclosing mantle, mantle usually fleshy and with calcareous plates; thoracic appendages simple, slender, and bristly, not leaflike, typically 6 pairs; abdomen much reduced, vestigial; structures variously reduced in parasites, ranging from lack of calcareous plates and reduction of appendages to a saclike mass without shell or appendages; marine, generally common on solid substrates, filter feeders or parasites.

Whale Barnacles (Order Thoracica)—calcareous plates reduced in size; body elongate, stalked; on whales.

Gooseneck Barnacles (Order Thoracica)—calcareous plates generally large, forming a shell; body elongate, stalked; widespread marine.

Acorn Barnacles (Order Thoracica)—calcareous plates generally large, forming a shell; body short, not stalked; widespread marine, including some on whales.

Parasitic Barnacles (Orders Acrothoracica, Rhizocephala, and Ascothoracica)—body parts variously reduced, partly associated with structures of marine animals, thereby parasitizing them, order Acrothoracica in corals and mollusk shells, order Rhizocephala on decapod crustacea and tunicates, and Ascothoracica on echinoderms and soft corals.

SUBCLASS MALACOSTRACA (Malacostracans)

Diagnosis: body typically of 19 segments, 5 head, 8 thorax (regularly covered by a carapace), 6 (rarely 7) abdomen; abdomen with appendages (except on rare 7th segment); mostly marine, also freshwater, terrestrial, and parasitic.

Superorder Leptostraca

Diagnosis: abdomen of 7 segments.

Order Nebaliacea (Visored Shrimps)

Diagnosis: carapace bivalved, with a hinged anterior plate that covers the head; marine filter feeders, usually in bottom mud or seaweeds.

Superorder Pericarida

Diagnosis: abdomen of 6 segments; carapace present or absent, if present not fused to 4 or more thoracic segments; females having brood pouches under the thorax; 2nd pair of thoracic appendages not raptorial.

Order Mysidacea (Ghost or Opossum Shrimps)

Diagnosis: carapace covers much of thorax; terminal tail appendages tending to form a fan; aquatic, mostly filter feeders.

Order Cumacea (Hooded Shrimps)

Diagnosis: carapace large, often with the 2 anterior plates joined over the head; marine burrowers in sand or mud, filter feeders.

Order Tanaidacea (Bottom Shrimps)

Diagnosis: carapace small; 2nd thoracic legs with pincers; aquatic, burrow in mud or construct tubes; filter feeders.

Order Isopoda (Sowbugs)

Diagnosis: no carapace; abdomen short, segments partly to completely fused; body generally flattened from top to bottom; aquatic and terrestrial, all crawl, many swim or burrow, mostly scavengers and/or herbivores, many parasites, especially of fish and crustaceans.

Suborder Gnathidiidea (Big-headed Sowbugs)

Diagnosis: head large; only 5 thoracic segments visible; abdomen short and narrower than thorax; marine, larval stage is an external fish parasite.

Suborder Anthuridea (Stick Sowbugs)

Diagnosis: body sticklike, long and cylindrical; aquatic, almost all are marine.

Suborder Flabellifera (Fan-tailed Sowbugs)

Diagnosis: body flattened, generally long and broad; tail appendages broad and flat, forming a distinctly fanlike tail; mostly marine (include the wood borers), a few freshwater.

Suborder Epicaridea (Crustacean Lice)

Diagnosis: parasites of marine and freshwater crustaceans; body flattened, asymmetrical in females; females with body segments fused and without appendages.

Suborder Valvifera (Kelp Sowbugs)

Diagnosis: body generally flattened; tail composed of a

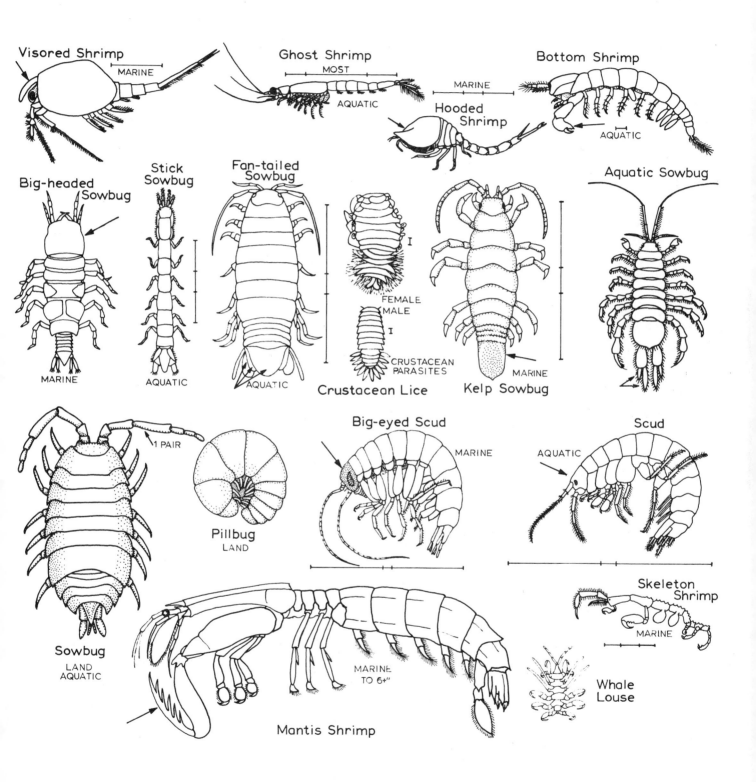

Visored Shrimp — MARINE

Ghost Shrimp — MOST — AQUATIC

Hooded Shrimp

Bottom Shrimp — MARINE — AQUATIC

Big-headed Sowbug — MARINE

Stick Sowbug — AQUATIC

Fan-tailed Sowbug — AQUATIC

Crustacean Lice — FEMALE — MALE — CRUSTACEAN PARASITES

Kelp Sowbug — MARINE

Aquatic Sowbug

Sowbug — LAND AQUATIC — 1 PAIR

Pillbug — LAND

Big-eyed Scud — MARINE

Scud — AQUATIC

Skeleton Shrimp — MARINE

Whale Louse

Mantis Shrimp — MARINE TO 6+"

single part rather than many separate segments *or* other parts are reduced to insignificance in size; marine, mostly on objects (especially seaweeds), also in crevices.

Suborder Asellota (Aquatic Sowbugs)

Diagnosis: body more-or-less flattened; abdomen terminated by a large plate which in turn has 2 appendages, each composed of a basal segment having 2 terminal segments; aquatic, includes most freshwater sowbugs.

Suborder Oniscoidea (Sowbugs, Strand Sowbugs, and Pillbugs)

Diagnosis: only 1 pair of conspicuous feelers, antennae well-developed, antennules vestigial.
Sowbugs (Families Oniscidae and Trichoniscidae)—body cannot be rolled into a ball; mostly terrestrial, rarely intertidal.
Strand Sowbugs (Family Ligiidae)—body cannot be rolled into a ball; amphibious between beach and sea.
Pillbugs (Family Armadillididae)—body can be rolled into a ball, a defensive reaction generally displayed when the animal is disturbed; terrestrial.

Order Amphipods (Scuds)

Diagnosis: no carapace; abdomen long, flexed between 3rd and 4th segments; body generally flattened from side to side; mostly marine (includes amphibious sand hoppers and beach fleas), many freshwater; most can swim, many burrow, many live in tubes; mostly scavengers, many predators.

Suborder Hyperiidea (Big-eyed Scuds)

Diagnosis: eyes large; head not fused to 2nd thoracic segment; marine, pelagic.

Suborder Gammaridea (Scuds)

Diagnosis: eyes moderate to small in size; head not fused to 2nd thoracic segment; marine, strand, and freshwater.

Suborder Caprellidea (Skeleton Shrimps and Whale Lice)

Diagnosis: eyes small; both 1st and 2nd thoracic segments fused to head; abdominal segments fused and reduced; some appendages reduced or absent; marine.
Skeleton Shrimps (Family Caprellidae)—body distinctly elongate; marine climbers, especially on hydroids and crest and crown animals.
Whale Lice (Family Cyamidae)—body not especially long; external parasites of whales.

Superorder Hoplocarida

Diagnosis: abdomen of 6 segments; carapace not fused to 4 thoracic segments; females without brood pouches;

2nd pair of thoracic appendages raptorial, resembling those of mantids.

Order Stomatopoda (Mantis Shrimps)

Diagnosis: body elongate, flattened from top to bottom; marine, mostly burrowers, also in rock crevices; predators on small fish and other crustaceans.

Superorder Eucarida

Diagnosis: abdomen of 6 segments; carapace fused to and covering all of thorax.

Order Euphausiacea (Translucent or Luminescent Shrimps)

Diagnosis: front thoracic appendages unspecialized, 7 pairs of walking legs; marine, pelagic; mostly filter feeders, a few predators.

Order Decapoda

Diagnosis: front thoric appendages specialized, associated with mouth parts, 5 pairs of walking legs which may or may not have pincers; aquatic or mostly so, some make land excursions and excavations but rely on water inundation; many sand and mud burrowers, some form tubes, other live in crevices or shells; mostly predators and/or scavengers, some filter and detritus feeders.

Suborder Natantia (Shrimp)

Diagnosis: body laterally compressed; abdomen well-developed, 1st and last segments about the same size; no pincers much larger than corresponding segments of other legs; includes most true swimmers among the decapods, most swim some.
Primitive Shrimp (Tribe Penaeidea)—lateral plates of 2nd abdominal segment do not overlap the 1st abdominal segment; marine.
Shrimp (Tribe Caridea)—lateral plates of 2nd abdominal segment overlap the 1st abdominal segment; aquatic, includes all freshwater shrimp.

Suborder Reptantia

Diagnosis: body often flattened from top to bottom, also cylindrical; abdomen well to poorly developed, 1st segment smaller than the last; pincers, if present, with 1 pair distinctly larger than corresponding segments of other legs; few truly swim.
Spiny Lobsters (Superfamily Scyllaridea)—body cylindrical, abdomen extended and well-developed; pincers absent; marine.
Crayfishes (Superfamily Nephropsidea)—body cylindrical, abdomen extended and well-developed; pincers present on 1st 3 pairs of legs; freshwater.
Lobsters (Superfamily Nephropsidea)—body cylindrical,

CRUSTACEANS III

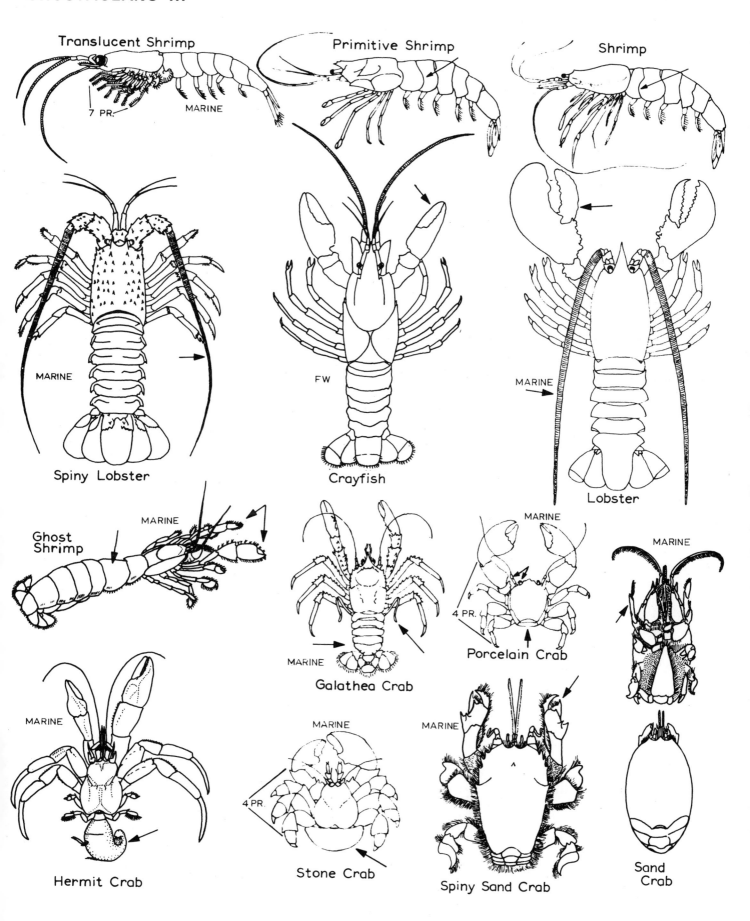

Translucent Shrimp
7 PR.
MARINE

Primitive Shrimp

Shrimp

Spiny Lobster
MARINE

Crayfish
FW

Lobster
MARINE

Ghost Shrimp
MARINE

Galathea Crab
MARINE

Porcelain Crab
MARINE
4 PR.

MARINE

Hermit Crab
MARINE

Stone Crab
MARINE
4 PR.

Spiny Sand Crab
MARINE

Sand Crab

abdomen extended and well-developed; pincers present on 1st 3 pairs of legs; marine, Atlantic.

Ghost Shrimps (Superfamily Thalassinidea)—carapace compressed; abdomen extended and well-developed; pincers on 1st 2 pairs of legs, 1st pair asymmetrical; marine burrowers.

Galathea Crabs (Superfamily Galatheidea)—crablike, abdomen symmetrical, flexed (but relatively loosely) under thorax; antennae external to eyes; 5th pair of legs reduced, folded into gill chambers; prominent spine projects forward from carapace; marine.

Porcelain Crabs (Superfamily Galatheidea)—crablike, abdomen symmetrical, flexed under thorax; antennae external to eyes; 5th pair of legs reduced, folded into gill chambers; carapace without a prominent forward-projecting spine; marine.

Hermit Crabs (Superfamily Paguridea)—abdomen asymmetrical, usually soft, long and twisted, not flexed under thorax; antennae external to eyes; marine, regularly found in univalve shells, twist of abdomen acts to hold shell.

Stone Crabs (Superfamily Paguridea)—crablike, abdomen flexed under thorax, but abdomen asymmetrical; antennae external to eyes; 5th pair of legs reduced, generally hidden; marine.

Spiny Sand Crabs (Superfamily Hippidea)—somewhat elongate but crablike, abdomen symmetrical, flexed under thorax; antennae external to eyes; 1st pair of legs without well-developed pincers; last joint of legs 2, 3 and 4 flattened; 5th pair of legs reduced, generally hidden; 2nd pair of legs with pincers; marine, in surf zone sand.

Sand Crabs (Superfamily Hippidea)—somewhat elongate but crablike, abdomen symmetrical, flexed under thorax; antennae external to eyes; 1st pair of legs without well-developed pincers; last joint of legs 2, 3, and 4 flattened; 5th pair of legs reduced, generally hidden; 2nd pair of legs without pincers; marine, in surf zone sand.

Short-Legged Crabs (Tribe Oxystomata)—crablike, abdomen symmetrical, reduced, tightly flexed under thorax; antennae internal to eyes; mouth field triangular, front of mouth closed; 4th and 5th pairs of legs reduced; marine.

Closed-Mouth Crabs (Tribe Oxystomata)—crablike, abdomen symmetrical, reduced, tightly flexed under thorax; antennae internal to eyes; mouth field triangular, front of mouth closed; no marked reduction in rear legs; marine.

Opened-Mouth Crabs (Tribe Oxystomata)——crablike, abdomen symmetrical, reduced, tightly flexed under thorax; antennae internal to eyes; mouth field triangular, front of mouth open; marine.

Horseman Crabs (Tribe Dromiacea)—crablike, abdomen symmetrical, reduced, tightly flexed under thorax; antennae internal to eyes; mouth field squarish; 5th pair of legs reduced; marine, includes forms that regularly use bivalve shells or sponges as movable covers.

Triangular Crabs (Tribe Brachygnatha)—crablike, abdomen symmetrical, reduced, tightly flexed under thorax; antennae internal to eyes; mouth field squarish; carapace somewhat triangular with pointed apex; large 1st and small 5th legs distinctive; marine.

Spider or Kelp Crabs (Tribe Brachygnatha)—crablike, abdomen symmetrical, reduced, tightly flexed under thorax; antennae internal to eyes; mouth field squarish; carapace somewhat pointed in front; pincers not greatly larger than corresponding parts on other legs; marine.

Rock Crabs (Tribe Brachygnatha)—crablike, abdomen symmetrical, reduced, tightly flexed under thorax; antennae internal to eyes; mouth field squarish; each antennule folded backward; marine, also semiterrestrial.

Swimming Crabs (Tribe Brachygnatha)—crablike, abdomen symmetrical, reduced, tightly flexed under thorax; antennae internal to eyes; mouth field squarish; last segment of 5th legs flattened, modified for swimming; marine.

Mud Crabs (Tribe Brachygnatha)—crablike, abdomen symmetrical, reduced, tightly flexed under thorax; antennae internal to eyes; mouth field squarish; antennules directed transversely, not backward; marine.

Shore Crabs (Tribe Brachygnatha)__crablike, abdomen symmetrical, reduced, tightly flexed under thorax; antennae internal to eyes; mouth field squarish; eyestalks heavy; marine, semiterrestrial.

Pea Crabs (Tribe Brachygnatha)—crablike, abdomen symmetrical, reduced, tightly flexed under thorax; antennae internal to eyes; mouth field squarish; carapace soft, pincers small; marine, regularly found living in animals.

Burrowing Crabs (Tribe Brachygnatha)—crablike, abdomen symmetrical, reduced, tightly flexed under thorax; antennae internal to eyes; mouth field squarish; carapace conspicuously fringed with "hairs" along front and sides; marine.

Fiddler Crabs (Tribe Brachygnatha)—crablike, abdomen symmetrical, reduced, tightly flexed under thorax; antennae internal to eyes; mouth field squarish; eyestalks long and slender; 1 pincer normally greatly enlarged; marine, often found above water line, "play the fiddle" with 1 pincer on the other.

Class Myriapoda (Myriapods)

Diagnosis: body elongate, somewhat wormlike; head with 1 pair of antennae and 1 or 2 pairs of maxillae; without a carapace; no distinct separation of body into a thorax and abdomen; terrestrial.

SUBCLASS DIPLOPODA (Millipedes)

Diagnosis: head with 1 pair of antennae and 1 pair of

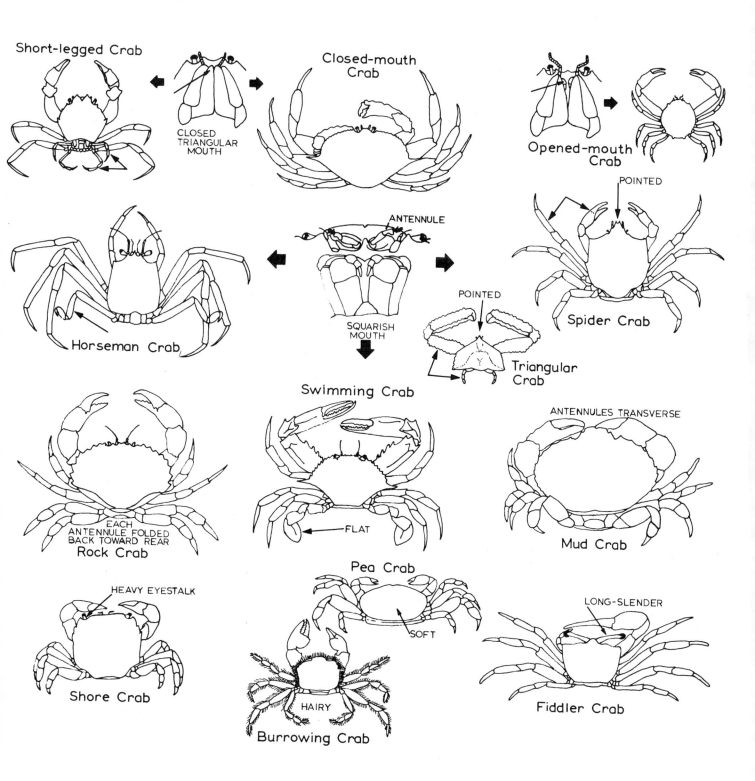

Short-legged Crab

CLOSED TRIANGULAR MOUTH

Closed-mouth Crab

Opened-mouth Crab

POINTED

Horseman Crab

ANTENNULE

SQUARISH MOUTH

POINTED

Spider Crab

Triangular Crab

Swimming Crab

EACH ANTENNULE FOLDED BACK TOWARD REAR
Rock Crab

FLAT

Pea Crab

ANTENNULES TRANSVERSE

Mud Crab

HEAVY EYESTALK

Shore Crab

SOFT

HAIRY

Burrowing Crab

LONG-SLENDER

Fiddler Crab

maxillae; body usually cylindrical, most segments with 2 pairs of legs; usually in damp places under objects or underground; scavengers and/or herbivores; sexes separate, eggs laid, young with 6 body segments and 3 pairs of legs, up to 10 molts to the adult form.

Order Polyxenida (Bristly Millipedes)

Diagnosis: adults with 13 pairs of legs; body covering soft; body hairs forming long lateral tufts; widespread but uncommon, usually found under bark.

Order Glomerida (Pill Millipedes)

Diagnosis: body with 14–16 segments, can be rolled into a ball; California, southern and southeastern United States.

Order Polydesmida (Flat-back Millipedes)

Diagnosis: body with 18–22 segments, back flattened; widespread.

Order Chordeumida (Bristle-tail Millipedes)

Diagnosis: body with 30 or more segments, last segment with 1–3 pairs of hair-tipped spinnerets, body rounded; widespread but mostly southern and western United States.

Order Opisthospermophora (Hooded Millipedes)

Diagnosis: body with 40 or more segments, last segment without spinnerets, body rounded; widespread but mostly southern and western United States.

Order Colobognatha (Small-head Millipedes)

Diagnosis: body with 30–60 segments, back flattened, head small; widespread.

SUBCLASS PAUROPODA (Humus Millipedes)

Diagnosis: head with 1 pair of 3-branched antennae and 1 pair of maxillae; body cylindrical, minute, of 11 (sometimes 12) segments, and with 9 (sometimes 10) pairs of legs (0–1 pair per segment); eyeless, whitish forms that resemble true millipedes; in damp places, under objects on the ground or in soil; herbivores, believed to feed on fungi, perhaps also scavengers; sexes separate, 4 larval stages, 1st having only 4 trunk segments and 3 pairs of legs.

SUBCLASS SYMPHYLA (Garden Centipedes)

Diagnosis: head with 1 pair of antennae and 2 pairs of maxillae; body cylindrical, short, of 15–22 segments, and with 10–12 pairs of legs (0–1 pair per segment); eyeless and centipedelike but centipedes have at least 15 pairs

of legs; active, whitish animals hidden in damp places that contain humus; mainly scavengers, also herbivores, feed upon vegetable matter in soil, sometimes damage cultivated plants or field crops; sexes separate, larvae with 6–7 pairs of legs.

SUBCLASS CHILOPODA (Centipedes)

Diagnosis: head with 1 pair of antennae and 2 pairs of maxillae; body flattened, with 15–181 segments (0–1 per segment); 1st pair of legs modified, hooklike, and with a poison duct leading to a terminal fang (bites rarely dangerous to man); usually under objects on the ground, under ground, or in other dark, moist places, predators, mainly on insects; sexes separate, egg laid or young born alive, 12 or more larval stages; larvae resemble adults, in long-legged and 30-legged centipedes' 1st larval stage there are 10 segments and 7 pairs of legs, in other centepedes' 1st larval stage there are as many segments and legs as in the adults.

Order Scutigeromorpha (Long-legged Centipedes)

Diagnosis: 15 pairs of legs, legs long; frequently enter houses.

Order Lithobiomorpha (30-legged Centipedes)

Diagnosis: 15 pairs of legs of normal length.

Order Scolopendromorpha (Giant Centipedes)

Diagnosis: 21–23 pairs of legs; includes the most venomous centipedes.

Order Geophilomorpha (Ground Centipedes)

Diagnosis: 29 or more pairs of legs; frequently found in soil.

Class Insecta (Insects)

Diagnosis: body with head, thorax, and abdomen distinct; head with 1 pair of antennae and mouthparts variously modified for chewing, sucking, or lapping; thorax of 3 segments, typically with 2 pairs of wings (also 1 pair or none) and 3 pairs of legs; abdomen usually 11 segments, but variable, without legs; widespread and very numerous in all habitats, but only a few are marine; reproduction generally with separate sexes (also parthenogenesis), eggs laid (also retained by female), and generally with 1 of 3 general plans of development:

(1) direct development—hatchlings and other immature stages resemble adults.

(2) gradual, simple, or incomplete metamorphosis—hatchlings and other immature stages, called nymphs, resemble adults but lack the size, body proportions, simple eyes, and wing size of adults.

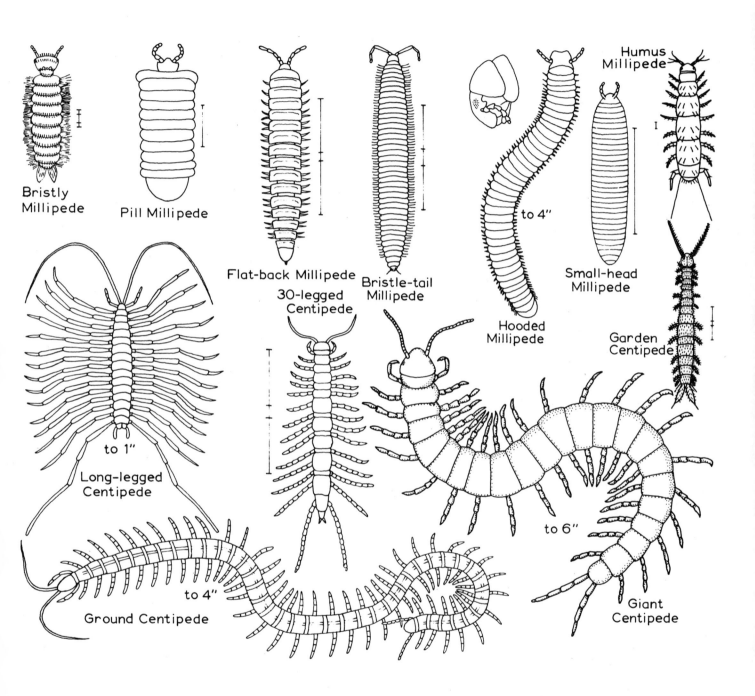

Bristly
Millipede

Pill Millipede

Flat-back Millipede

30-legged
Centipede

Bristle-tail
Millipede

Hooded
Millipede

to 4"

Humus
Millipede

Small-head
Millipede

Garden
Centipede

to 1"
Long-legged
Centipede

Ground Centipede

to 4"

to 6"

Giant
Centipede

95

(3) complete or complex metamorphosis—hatchlings and early immatures are wormlike, called larvae (include caterpillars); larvae transform into a nonfeeding, usually inactive stage, the pupa (includes the chrysalis of butterflies), which transforms into the adult.

SUBCLASS APTERYGOTA (Apterous Insects)

Diagnosis: usually with bristlelike appendages on the underside of the abdomen; wingless and not derived from winged ancestors; development direct, little or no change in form between hatchlings and adults.

Order Protura (Proturans)

Diagnosis: minute; whitish, without eyes, wings, or antennae; in moist places, under and among surface objects, and in soil; scavengers.

Order Thysanura (Bristletails)

Diagnosis: 2–3 appendages on the end of the abdomen; occur in a wide range of habitats; represent all feeding habits.
Primitive Bristletails (Family Lepidotrichidae)—resemble bristletails but without body scales; rare, under decaying Douglas fir bark and wood in northern California; 1 living species known, named in 1961.
Bristletails (Family Lepismatidae)—abdomen terminated by 3 hairlike processes; eyes small; body covered by scales; includes the silverfish and firebrat; in buildings, caves, and ant nests, under or in ground debris; mostly scavengers.
Jumping Bristletails (Family Machilidae)—abdomen terminated by 3 hairlike processes; eyes large; body covered by scales; generally in grassy or wooded areas under or among plant debris or rocks; mostly scavengers.
Forktails (Family Campodeidae)—abdomen terminated by 2, generally hairlike, processes, as long as antennae, many segmented; in damp places, under or in ground debris; mostly scavengers.
Stubby Forktails (Family Anajapygidae)—abdomen terminated by 2 stubby processes, shorter than antennae, segmented; in damp places, under or in ground debris; mostly scavengers; 1 known species from California, considered rare but locally fairly common.
Forcepstails (Family Japygidae)—abdomen terminated by 2 processes (forcepslike in adults), shorter than antennae, 1 segment; in damp places, under or in ground debris; mostly scavengers.

Order Collembola (Springtails)

Diagnosis: mostly minute; most with a unique springing organ on underside of abdomen, may jump to more than 15 times their length; in decaying matter under damp objects, sometimes on freshwater surfaces or along sea shores; usually appear in great numbers during the winter breeding season; may congregate on sidewalks, lawns, pools, or even snow; includes the remarkable ice-inhabiting snow and glacier fleas; scavengers or herbivores, sometimes damage plants.

SUBCLASS PTERYGOTA: DIVISION EXOPTERYGOTA

Diagnosis: without bristlelike appendages on the underside of the abdomen; winged or from winged ancestors; life cycle characterized by simple metamorphosis, young are nymphs.

Order Odonata (Dragonflies and Damselflies)

Diagnosis: 4 wings, transparent and membranous, elongate, with many cross veins, held laterally (dragonflies) or vertically (damselflies) at rest; antennae very short, awl-shaped; mouthparts chewing, toothlike; nymphs in freshwater, feeding on mosquito larvae to small fish; adults terrestrial, usually not far from fresh water, normally seen on the wing, feeding on insects.
Dragonflies (Superfamily Aeshnoidea)—hind wings wider at base than fore wings; wings horizontal at rest; wing triangles (stippled in drawing) similar in size, shape, and position.
Skimmers (Superfamily Libelluloidea)—hind wings wider at base than fore wings; wings horizontal at rest; wing triangles (stippled in drawing) differ in position and usually in size and shape.
Narrow-Winged Damselflies (Superfamily Coenagrioidea)—wings similar in size and shape, usually held together above body at rest; 2, rarely 3, antenodal cross veins.
Broad-Winged Damselflies (Superfamily Agrioidea)—wings similar in size and shape, usually held together above body at rest; 10 or more antenodal cross veins.

Order Orthoptera (Orthopterans)

Diagnosis: 4, 2, or 0 wings; fore wings usually thickened, opaque, long and narrow; hind wings membranous and transparent, broad, fold like a fan; 2 wings in pigmy grasshoppers, forewings reduced to scales; mouthparts chewing; nymphs and adults widespread on land, mostly scavengers and predators; many make snapping or buzzing noises during flight (hind wing movements), many males sing by rubbing the hind legs against the fore wings.
Pigmy Mole Crickets (Family Tridactylidae)—hind femora thicker than middle, for jumping; front legs enlarged, strongly flattened; antennae less than 1/2 inch; mostly burrowers, usually in sand along lakes and streams, also found on surface.
Pigmy Grasshoppers or Grouse Locusts (Family Tetrigidae)—hind femora thicker than middle, for jumping; pronotum very long, nearly to or beyond tip of abdomen;

APTEROUS INSECTS

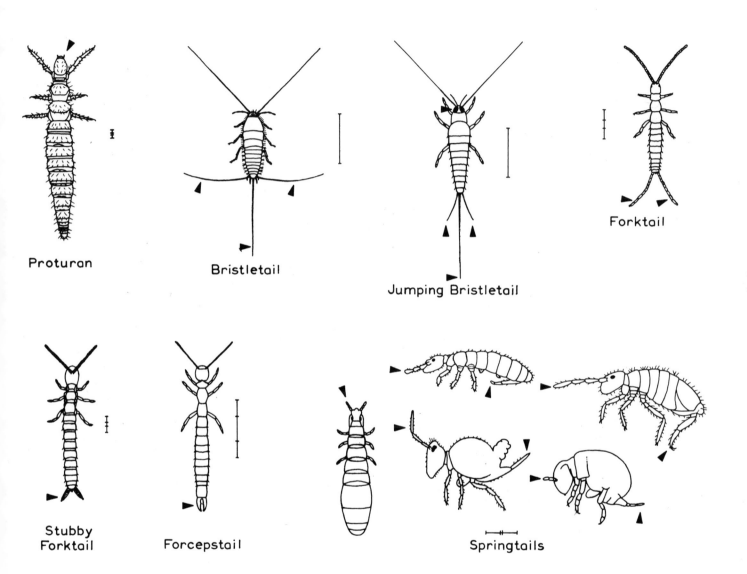

Proturan

Bristletail

Jumping Bristletail

Forktail

Stubby
Forktail

Forcepstail

Springtails

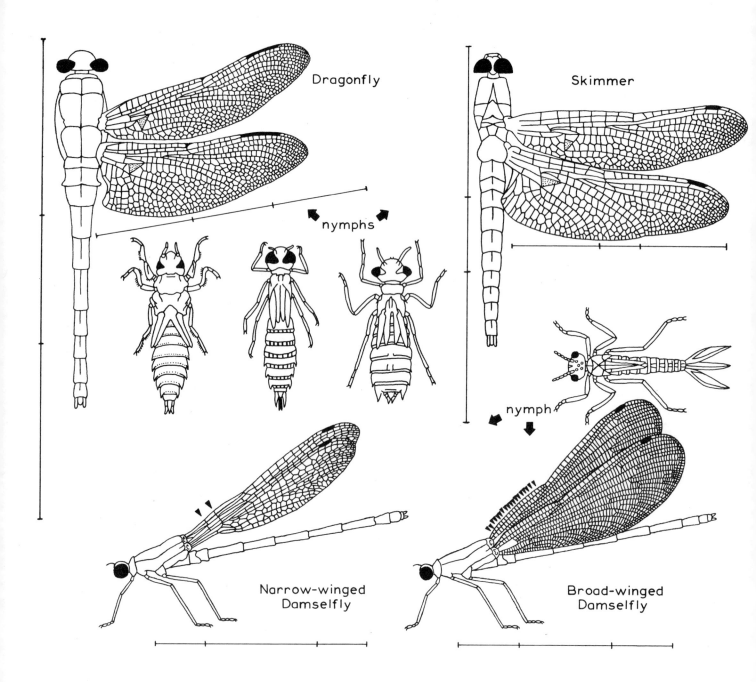

Dragonfly

Skimmer

nymphs

nymph

Narrow-winged
Damselfly

Broad-winged
Damselfly

mostly in open areas except in winter (under forest litter or sod), some live near water (can swim), one of few grasshoppers that overwinter as adults.

Short-Horned Grasshoppers (Family Acrididae)—hind femora thicker than middle, for jumping; antennae not reaching end of abdomen but longer than front femur; includes most grasshoppers common in grassy and roadside areas from summer to fall; generally in grassy or open areas, often near water, a few overwinter as adults; some periodically increase to great numbers, become migratory, and devastate crops; generally considered true locusts.

Monkey Grasshoppers (Family Eumastacidae)—hind femora thicker than middle, for jumping; antennae not reaching end of abdomen, shorter than front femur; extend northward from tropics to southwestern state mountains, north to San Francisco, southern Nevada, and central Arizona; inhabit shrub habitat (chaparral), usually found on uppermost branches.

Desert Grasshoppers (Family Eumastacidae)—hind femora thicker than middle, for jumping; female antennae not reaching end of abdomen, male antennae longer than abdomen; nocturnal, probably not encountered during daylight hours; range and habitat similar to that of monkey grasshoppers.

Cone-Headed Grasshoppers or Locusts (Family Tettigoniidae, Subfamily Copiphorinae)—hind femora thicker than middle, for jumping; antennae clearly longer than abdomen; head extended forward as a distinct cone, usually excavated and toothed below; color green or brown; generally in tall herbs, grass or weeds; sluggish forms whose bite can draw blood.

Meadow Grasshoppers or Locusts (Family Tettigoniidae, Subfamily Conocephalinae)—hind femora thicker than middle, for jumping; antennae clearly longer than abdomen; head extended forward as a rounded tubercle with concave sides; color usually greenish; generally in moist areas, meadows or along ponds and streams.

Short-Winged, Bush, or Round-Headed Katydids (Family Tettigoniidae, Subfamily Phaneropterinae)—hind femora thicker than middle, for jumping; antennae clearly longer than abdomen; head essentially blunt in front; hind wings usually longer than fore wings or tip of fore wing appears cut off at an angle; pronotum narrow, not long and shieldlike; normally green, also pink, often found on shrubs.

Shield-Backed Katydids (Family Tettigoniidae, Subfamily Decticinae)—hind femora thicker than middle, for jumping; antennae clearly longer than abdomen; head essentially blunt in front; wings, if present, usually with fore wings longer than hind wings, wings usually short or absent; pronotum usually broad and shieldlike; color brownish to black; most resemble crickets; normally inhabit fields or woods; some western forms may destroy crops, includes the Mormon cricket.

Hump-Winged Crickets (Family Tettigoniidae, Subfamily Prophalangopsinae)—hind femora thicker than middle, for jumping; antennae clearly longer than abdomen; head essentially blunt in front; antennae attached very low on front of head; wings reduced, appear abnormal, color brownish to black, resemble crickets; western, uncommon.

Katydids (Family Tettigoniidae, Subfamily Tettigoniinae)—hind femora thicker than middle, for jumping; antennae clearly longer than abdomen; head essentially blunt in front; forewing long and leaflike and longer than hindwing; color green; mostly in tree and shrub foilage.

Leaf-Rolling Crickets (Family Gryllacrididae, Subfamily Gryllacridinae)—hind femora thicker than middle, for jumping; antennae clearly longer than abdomen; head essentially blunt in front; tarsi of first 2 pairs of legs lobed beneath; eyes elongate, oval; color grayish or brownish; rare, in East, seldom north of Indiana or New Jersey; nocturnal, form nests by rolling and tying leaves with silk; mostly predaceous on aphids.

Camel or Cave Crickets (Family Gryllacrididae, Subfamily Rhaphidophorinae)—hind femora thicker than middle, for jumping; antennae clearly longer than abdomen; head essentially blunt in front; hump-backed; pronotum not much larger than following 2 plates; color brownish; frequents moist places, in caves and in and under ground objects.

Jerusalem, Sand, or Stone Crickets (Family Gryllacrididae, Subfamily Stenopelmatinae)—hind femora thicker than middle, for jumping; antennae clearly longer than abdomen; head essentially blunt in front; abdomen inflated, marked with black bands; color brown; usually in loose soil, often found under objects.

Ant Crickets (Family Gryllidae, Subfamily Myrmecophilinae)—hind femora thicker than middle, for jumping; antennae clearly longer than abdomen; head essentially blunt in front; tarsi 3-segmented; body broad; wingless; pronotum generally covering back of head; darkish; minute; in ant nests.

Bush Crickets (Family Gryllidae, Subfamily Eneopterinae)—hind femora thicker than middle, for jumping; antennae clearly longer than abdomen; head essentially blunt in front; tarsi 3-segmented; body broad; front wings bent down sharply at sides; pronotum generally covering back of head; pronotum relatively long; usually brownish; generally on woody plants.

Crickets (Family Gryllidae, part)—hind femora thicker than middle, for jumping; antennae clearly longer than abdomen; head essentially blunt in front; tarsi 3-segmented; body broad; front wings bent down sharply at sides; pronotum generally covering back of head; pronotum of moderate length; color brownish to black; widespread from dry to moist situations, in houses, bushes, and along roadsides, in grasslands or meadows, under debris, even underground (often found together in numbers).

Tree Crickets (Family Gryllidae, Subfamily Oecanthi-

ORTHOPTERANS

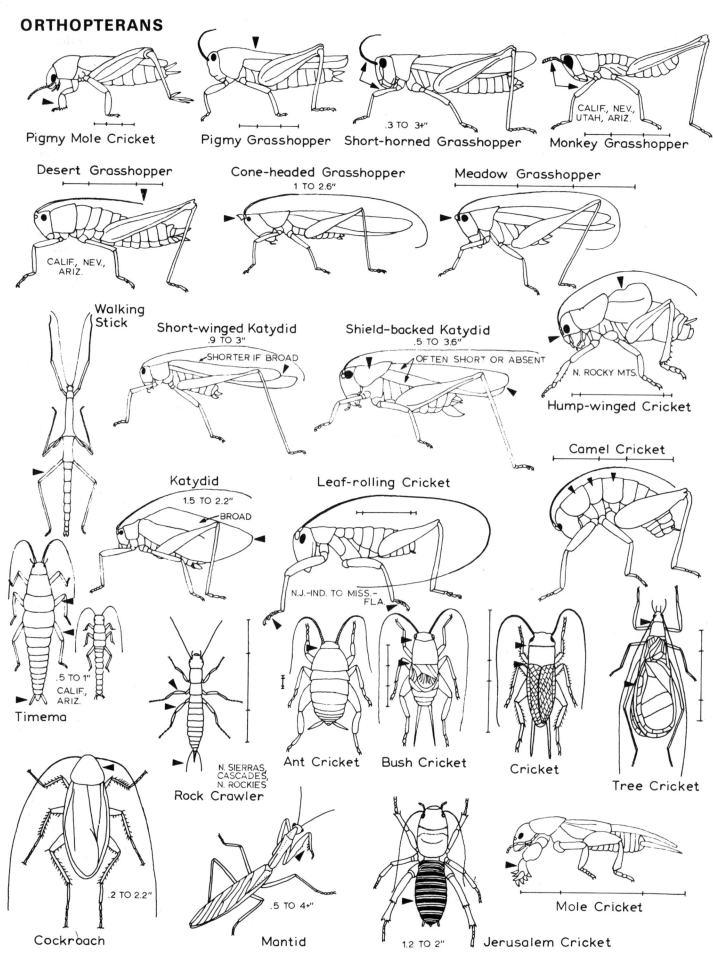

Pigmy Mole Cricket

Pigmy Grasshopper

Short-horned Grasshopper
.3 TO 3+"

Monkey Grasshopper
CALIF., NEV., UTAH, ARIZ.

Desert Grasshopper
CALIF., NEV., ARIZ.

Cone-headed Grasshopper
1 TO 2.6"

Meadow Grasshopper

Walking Stick

Short-winged Katydid
.9 TO 3"
SHORTER IF BROAD

Shield-backed Katydid
.5 TO 3.6"
OFTEN SHORT OR ABSENT

Hump-winged Cricket
N. ROCKY MTS.

Camel Cricket

Katydid
1.5 TO 2.2"
BROAD

Leaf-rolling Cricket
N.J.-IND. TO MISS.-FLA.

Timema
.5 TO 1"
CALIF., ARIZ.

Rock Crawler
N. SIERRAS, CASCADES, N. ROCKIES

Ant Cricket

Bush Cricket

Cricket

Tree Cricket

Cockroach
.2 TO 2.2"

Mantid
.5 TO 4+"

Jerusalem Cricket
1.2 TO 2"

Mole Cricket

nae)—hind femora thicker than middle, for jumping; antennae clearly longer than abdomen; head essentially blunt in front; tarsi 3-segmented; body broad; front wings bent down sharply at sides; pronotum generally covering back of head; pronotum relatively short; wings large, narrow at base; whitish to pale green; live in trees, in shrubs (may damage twigs), and in grassy or weedy areas.

Mole Crickets (Family Gryllidae, Subfamily Gryllotalpinae)—hind femora thicker than middle, for jumping; front legs enlarged, strongly flattened, modified for digging; antennae longer than 1/2 inch; resemble but are larger than pigmy mole crickets; color brownish; burrowers, in most places.

Walking Stick (Family Phasmidae)—hind femora not appreciably thicker than middle femora; tail bristles short; more than 1 1/2 inch long; generally on trees or shrubs, rarely cause damage; one of the few insects that can regenerate lost legs; protective mechanisms include a foul-odor chemical.

Timemas (Family Phasmidae)—hind femora not appreciably thicker than middle femora; tail bristles short; less that 1 1/4 inch long; color green or pinkish; on trees or shrubs in Pacific States.

Rock Crawlers (Family Grylloblattidae)—hind femora not appreciably thicker than middle femora; tail bristles long; rare under objects or in snow, found in mountains at elevations over 4,000 feet, often near snow, or water; in mountains of western Canada and California.

Cockroaches or Roaches (Family Blattidae)—body usually flattened, oval; head partly to completely covered by pronotum; widespread in a variety of situations, generally found under objects, in crevices, or emerging from retreats; include house invaders that eat and contaminate food, and produce unpleasant odors.

Mantids or Praying Mantids (Family Mantidae)—front legs jacknifelike, modified for grasping prey; voracious predators upon insects including other mantids; habit of holding forelegs together and upraised while waiting for prey is source of common names of praying mantid and soothsayer; generally encountered on trees or shrubs, especially deciduous ones in late fall or early winter.

Order Plecoptera (Stoneflies)

Diagnosis: 4 wings (reduced or absent in a few males) transparent and membraneous, hind wings broader than fore wings; wings held pleated and flat on back at rest; abdomen terminated by a pair of bristles, usually elongate; monthparts chewing; nymphs generally under stones in lakes and streams; predaceous, herbivorous or omnivorous; adult occurrence and feeding habits variable, generally near streams, more herbivorous than nymphs, some short-lived and never feed; widely preyed upon by freshwater predators, desirable bait for fishing.

Order Dermaptera (Earwigs)

Diagnosis: usually 4 wings, fore wings short, veinless, and leathery, hind wings (if present) longer, with radiating veins, transparent and membraneous; abdomen terminated by pincers; chewing mouthparts; nocturnal, hiding in cracks and crevices or under objects during the day, often common in garbage or damp places; mostly scavengers, also herbivores or predators, often harmful plant pests; form and can squirt a foul-smelling chemical a few inches; eggs laid in crevices or like areas and guarded by females; adults can survive winters.

Order Isoptera (Termites)

Diagnosis: 4 transparent and membranous wings during a brief stage of the life cycle or none; body soft, generally white or whitish; colonial; chewing mouthparts; social insects (also ants, wasps, and bees) characterized by a caste system, 2–6 (usually 4):

(1) reproductives (kings and queens) have fully developed wings (shed after mating), compound eyes, and usually pigmentation.

(2) workers (nymphs and sterile males and females) are wingless, lack compound eyes, and are pale in color.

(3) soldiers (sterile males and females) have greatly enlarged heads and mouthparts.

(4) supplementary reproductives (fertile males and females) also reproduce, but have shorter wings, usually smaller eyes, and less pigmentation that reproductives.

(5) adults (fertile males and females) resemble workers in appearance but can reproduce.

(6) nasuti (sterile males and females) have a narrow snout that is used to squirt a sticky secretion at an intruder.

Distribution associated with wood, some in moist situations underground, others in dry wood situations above ground, both types can cause severe damage to buildings. Feed upon cast skins, wastes, and remains of their kind, primarily feed on wood; can ingest wood cellulose because cellulose-digesting protozoans are present in their digestive tracts.

Order Embioptera (Webspinners)

Diagnosis: males usually winged, transparent and membranous, also reduced or absent; females wingless; body elongate, soft, but straight-sided; chewing mouthparts; rare, a few species in southern states; locally common in California; mostly colonial forms living in runways in debris, cracks, under bark, or among plants, runways lined with silk; mainly plant scavengers.

Order Psocoptera (Corrodentia) (Booklice)

Diagnosis: 4 membranous and transparent wings or none; chewing mouthparts; most frequently encountered in dwellings, often in books or papers, indoor forms wing-

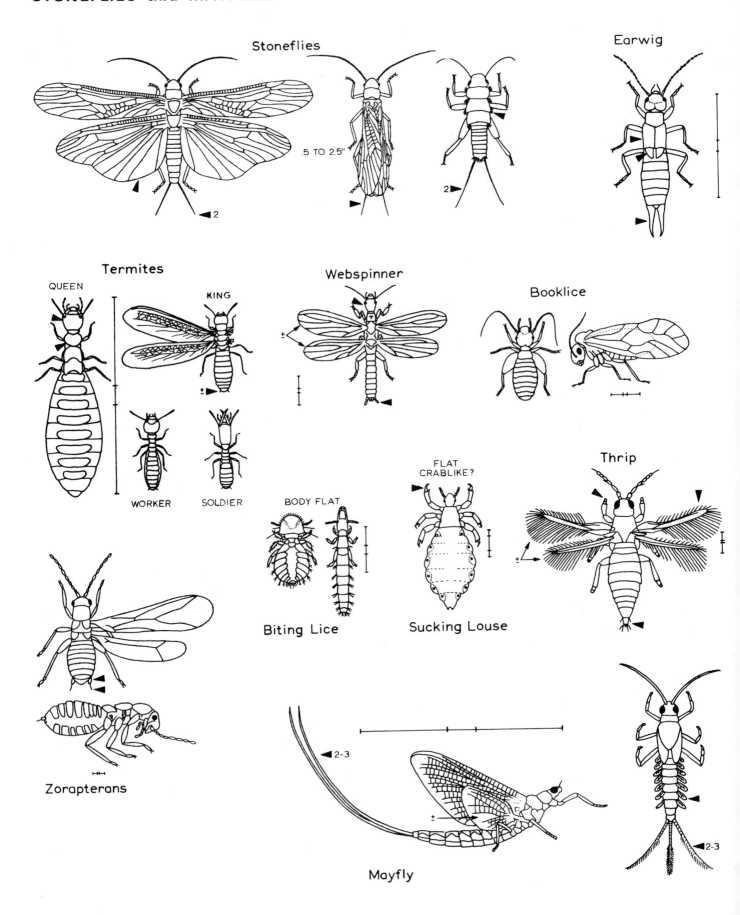

Stoneflies

.5 TO 2.5"

Earwig

Termites

QUEEN

KING

WORKER   SOLDIER

Webspinner

Booklice

Thrip

FLAT
CRABLIKE?

BODY FLAT

Biting Lice   Sucking Louse

Zorapterans

Mayfly

less, rarely cause damage; most species winged and live on trees or shrubs, or under bark or stones; feed on molds, other fungi, pollen, cereals, and dead organisms.

Order Zoraptera (Zorapterans)

Diagnosis: 4 membranous and transparent wings or none, shed as in royal ants and termites; resemble termites but pronotum is longer than head; rare, 2 United States species, from Maryland, Illinois, Arkansas and Oklahoma south to Texas and Florida; commonly associated with wood, frequently near termites; probably scavengers.

Order Mallophaga (Biting Lice)

Diagnosis: wingless; body flattened; chewing (piercing and biting) mouthparts; external parasites of birds and mammals, feeding upon hair, feathers, and skin, not known to infest man.

Order Anopleura (Sucking Lice)

Diagnosis: wingless; body flattened; piercing and sucking mouthparts; tarsi 1 segment, with 1 very large claw; external parasites on mammal blood and transmit various diseases including typhus and trench fevers; no true metamorphosis; includes the human louse, or "cootie."

Order Thysanoptera (Thrips)

Diagnosis: 4 wings present, reduced, or absent; wings long and narrow, alike, few or no veins, fringed with long hairs; mouthparts conical, rasping and sucking; commonly found on plants; mainly plant feeders, destroying many plants by feeding or introducing disease; some predators on small arthropods, a few bite man; commonly parthenogenetic.

Order Ephemeroptera (Mayflies)

Diagnosis: wings membranous and transparent, 4 or 2, fore wings large and triangular, hind wings small and rounded, all held up at rest; abdomen terminated by 2 or 3 hairlike tails; chewing mouth parts, but much reduced; nymphs widespread in fresh water, have up to 21 molts, live up to 3 years, herbivorous; adults not found far from fresh water, live a few hours or days, do not feed; act as prey for many aquatic insects and vertebrates; used as one of the patterns for fishing "flies" or lures.

Order Hemiptera (Bugs)

Diagnosis: 4 wings or wingless; forewings with base thickened, leathery or horny, and with apex membraneous and generally transparent; hind wings membraneous and transparent; wings crossed at rest; mouthparts piercing and sucking, composed of a beak (a slender, segmented structure) that arises at the front of the head and generally extends back along the underside of the body; a large group of common freshwater and terrestrial insects; some are beneficial predators on harmful insects, some are definitely harmful; some are blood-sucking, carrying diseases of man and other animals; many suck plant juices, thereby reducing plant vigor and introducing disease.

Water Boatmen (Family Corixidae)—antennae short; body oval, flattened; hind legs oarlike; eyes large; head about as broad as pronotum (conspicuous part of thorax); mostly fresh water, also brackish pools above high tide line; mostly scoop microorganisms with front tarsi, also predaceous on small aquatic animals; one of few aquatic bugs that do not bite.

Backswimmers (Family Notonectidae)—antennae short; body oval, flattened; hind legs oarlike, much longer than other legs; freshwater; predaceous, even on small fish and tadpoles; bite similar to a bee sting; swim on their backs.

Water Scorpions (Family Nepidae)—antennae short; front legs rapitorial; hind legs not flattened; freshwater, frequently on plants; slow-moving predators; bite painful.

Giant Water Bugs (Family Belostomatidae)—antennae short; front legs rapitorial; hind legs broad and flattened; freshwater, both nymphs and adults, but adults sometimes fly on land (attracted to lights enough to be called electric light bugs); predators, generally on larger animals, including small fish, salamanders, and frogs; bite very painful.

Creeping Water Bugs (Family Naucoridae)—antennae short; front legs rapitorial; membrane of fore wings without veins; freshwater, generally on quiet water plants; predators on small animals; bite painful.

Toad Bugs (Family Gelastocoridae)—antennae short; toadlike; eyes protruding; generally along margin of fresh water, often hopping; predators, mostly on small insects.

Water Striders (Family Gerridae)—antennae long; long-legged, hind legs extending well beyond abdomen; freshwater, generally on surface; predators and scavengers on insects falling on water surface.

Riffle Striders or Broad-Shouldered Water Striders (Family Veliidae)—antennae long; long-legged but hind legs barely, if at all, extending beyond abdomen; freshwater, often in or near riffles; predators on small animals.

Bed Bugs (Family Cimicidae)—antennae long; flat, broadly oval, wingless, external parasites of birds and mammals; during day hide in beds and/or crevices; blood feeders, apparently do not carry diseases.

Flower or Minute Pirate Bugs (Family Anthocoridae)—antennae long; fore wing with a distinctive area; most with black and white markings; most on plants, others in ground debris; predators on small insects and insect eggs.

Leaf or Plant Bugs (Family Miridae)—antennae long; only common bugs with a distinctive triangular piece attached to thickened part of fore wing; on plants, often abundant; mostly herbivorous, often causing great damage, some predaceous on small insects.

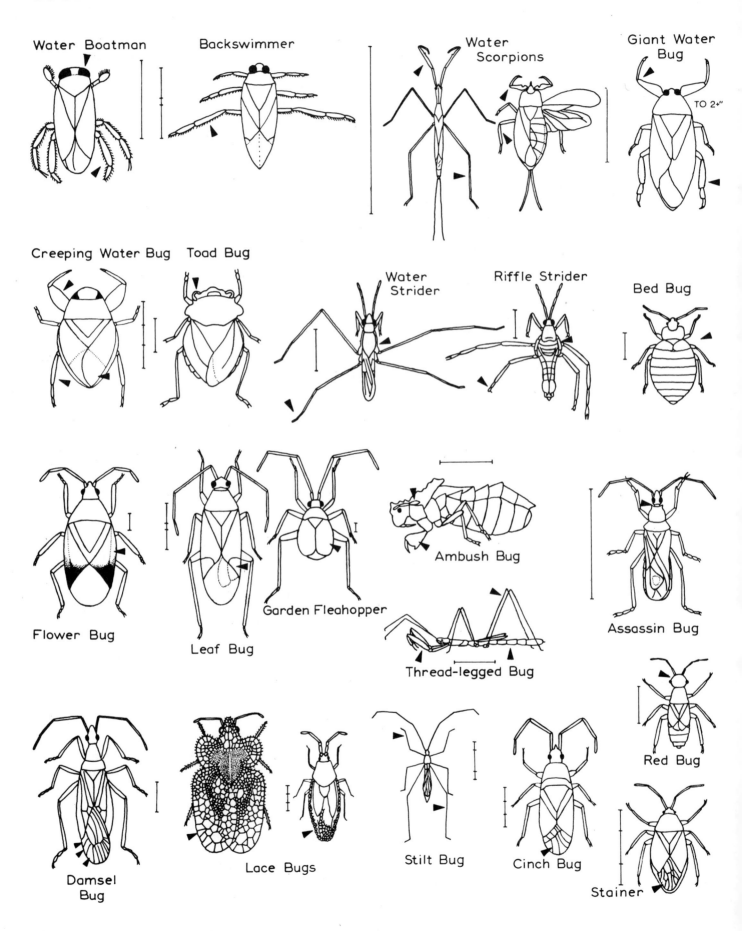

Water Boatman

Backswimmer

Water Scorpions

Giant Water Bug

TO 2+"

Creeping Water Bug

Toad Bug

Water Strider

Riffle Strider

Bed Bug

Flower Bug

Leaf Bug

Garden Fleahopper

Ambush Bug

Thread-legged Bug

Assassin Bug

Red Bug

Damsel Bug

Lace Bugs

Stilt Bug

Cinch Bug

Stainer

Garden Fleahoppers (Family Miridae)—antennac long; beetlelike, including fore wings (usually horny and leathery and lack apical membrane); on plants; herbivorous, damaging many cultivated plants.

Ambush Bugs (Family Phymatidae)—antennae long; last segment of antennae swollen; raptorial front legs with femora at least half as broad as long; on plants, hidden to ambush relatively large insects (flies, wasps, bees, etc.).

Assassin Bugs (Family Reduviidae)—antennae long; front legs raptorial; head with a necklike part; beak fits into a groove on underside of body; body robust; widespread on land; mostly predators and on insects; some blood-sucking, a few biting man (carry Chagas disease in South America—disease rare but known in the United States), rarely cause human deaths (as do bees, wasps, etc.) and only when people become allergic to the bite.

Thread-Legged Bugs (Family Ploiariidae)—antennae long; front legs raptorial; body very slender, long-legged; resemble walking sticks; in and about infrequently used buildings and cellars, also under ground objects and in short grass tufts; predators on insects.

Damsel Bugs (Family Nabidae)—antennae long; front legs raptorial; front femora enlarged; membrane of fore wing with many marginal cells created by venation; terrestrial insect predators.

Lace Bugs (Family Tingidae)—antennae long; fore wings with a lacelike pattern; nymphs usually spiny and without lacelike pattern; on plants; herbivorous, feeding damage, mostly to woody plants, causes yellow-spotting, complete browning, and finally dropping of leaves.

Stilt Bugs (Family Neididae)—antennae long; body slender, long-legged; generally among dense herbs; herbivores.

Cinch Bugs (Family Lygaeidae)—antennae long; head variable, elongate to triangular to short and broad; 4 or 5 simple veins in membranous part of fore wing; mostly on plants and herbivorous, some causing severe damage to cereals; a few insect predators.

Red Bugs (Family Pyrrhocoridae)—antennae long; head round; membranous part of fore wing reduced; usually colored bright red and black; often antlike, otherwise resemble stainers; on plants, herbivorous.

Stainers (Family Pyrrhocoridae)—antennae long; resemble cinch bugs but venation is more complex; usually colored bright red and black; generally on plants in large numbers; herbivorous; feeding activities generally stain plants, including cotton fibers.

Squash Bugs (Family Coreidae)—antennae long; membrane of fore wing with many veins; usually dark-colored and over .4 inch long; generally on plants; herbivorous or predaceous, mostly on insects.

Leaf-Footed Bugs (Family Coreidae)—antennae long; membrane of fore wing with many veins; usually dark-colored and over .4 inch long; some legs flattened, usually leaflike; generally on plants; herbivorous or predaceous, mostly on insects.

Grass Bugs (Family Corizidae)—antennae long; membrane of fore wing with many veins; usually light-colored and less than .4 inch long; on plants, herbivorous; often enter houses in the fall.

Broad-Headed Bugs (Family Coriscidae)—antennae long; membrane of fore wing with many (less than leaf-footed and grass bugs) veins; head almost as long and wide as pronotum; often stink more than stink bugs; on plants, mostly weeds; herbivorous.

Flat or Fungus Bugs (Family Aradidae)—antennae long; body very flat; wings small, not covering entire abdomen; under loose bark or decaying wood; primarily feed on fungi.

Shore Bugs (Family Saldidae)—antennae long; membrane of fore wing with 4 or 5 long cells created by venation; common along fresh- and saltwater shores, some burrowers; typical habit of flying short distances and hiding in shelters when disturbed; predaceous, generally on insects.

Water Treaders (Family Mesoveliidae)—antennae long; body small and slender; membrane of fore wing without veins; generally crawling on freshwater vegetation or floating logs; when disturbed, move rapidly on water surface; predators on small animals.

Water Measurers or Marsh Treaders (Family Hydrometridae)—antennae long; head long and slender, with bulging eyes; resemble walking sticks; walk slowly over shallow, freshwater organisms or surfaces; feed on minute organisms.

Burrower Bugs (Family Cydnidae)—antennae long; scutellum triangular; leg joint (tibia) with strong spines; usually black; burrowers, generally under objects, about plants or in sand; sometimes found in ant nests.

Negro Bugs (Family Corimelaenidae)—antennae long; scutellum very large, U-shaped; black and usually beetlelike; on plants, herbivorous.

Shield Bugs (Family Scutelleridae)—antennae long; scutellum very large, U-shaped; mostly brownish; on plants, mostly in woods, herbivorous.

Terrestrial Turtle Bugs (Family Podopidae)—antennae long; scutellum large, U-shaped; pronotum with prominent tooth on each side; mostly brownish; uncommon.

Stink Bugs (Family Pentatomidae)—antennae long; scutellum triangular; legs without strong spines; colors mostly bright and contrasting; commonest bugs having an unpleasant odor; widespread, often on plants; herbivores, predators, or omnivores; often plant pests, including farm crop pests.

Order Homoptera (Cicadas, Hoppers, Scale Insects, etc.)

Diagnosis: 4 wings or wingless, membranous and of like texture throughout, generally transparent, roofed over abdomen at rest; mouthparts piercing and sucking, composed of a beak (a slender, segmented structure) that arises at the back of the head; a large group generally associated with plants, herbivorous; many are serious plant pests, a few transmitting disease.

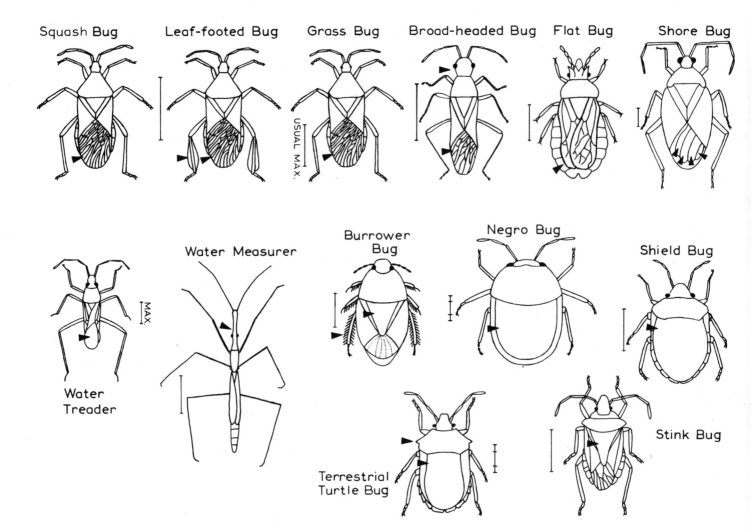

Squash Bug

Leaf-footed Bug

Grass Bug

USUAL MAX.

Broad-headed Bug

Flat Bug

Shore Bug

Water Measurer

Burrower Bug

Negro Bug

Shield Bug

MAX.

Water Treader

Terrestrial Turtle Bug

Stink Bug

Cicadas (Family Cicadidae)—both adults winged; tarsi 3-segmented; antennae very short, bristlelike; antennae arising from front of head between eyes; males with characteristic song; up to 17 years as nymphs, about a month as adults; adults herbivorous, eggs laid on twigs, nymph drops and burrows into soil, feeding on roots, last nymph stage emerges from ground, climbs on object (usually woody), fastens claws to object, and adult emerges from nymphal skin; egg-laying activities generally cause most damage to plants but large outbreaks of adults can do great damage, especially to woody plants.

Treehoppers (Family Membracidae)—both adults winged; tarsi 3-segmented; antennae very short, bristlelike; antennae arising from front of head between eyes; pronotum generally ornate, protrudes backward over abdomen; feed mostly on shrubs and trees.

Leafhoppers (Family Cicadellidae)—both adults winged; tarsi 3-segmented; antennae very short, bristlelike; antennae arising from front of head between eyes; hind tibia with 1 or more rows of small spines; many produce and exude a honeydew; include many forms causing damage to plants.

Spittlebugs or Froghoppers (Family Cercopidae)—both adults winged; tarsi 3-segmented; antennae very short, bristlelike; antennae arising from front of head between eyes; hind tibia with 1 or 2 prominent spines; hop, many vaguely frog-shaped, others resemble leafhoppers; nymph generally on plants within a frothy spittlelike mass, commonly found in herbaceous areas.

Planthoppers (Superfamily Fulgoroidea)—both adults winged; tarsi 3-segmented; antennae very short, bristlelike; antennae arising from side of head below eyes; few cause serious plant damage.

Jumping Plant Lice (Superfamily Psylloidea)—both adults winged; tarsi 2-segmented, with 2 claws; antennae long and hairlike; front wings usually thicker than hind wings; jumping forms usually thicker hind femora; usually resemble cicadas; some nymphs resemble certain plant lice by producing a wax; some transmit virus diseases to commercial plants.

Whiteflies (Superfamily Aleyrodoidea)—both adults winged; tarsi 2-segmented, with 2 claws; antennae long and hairlike; vaguely mothlike; wings about same size, usually opaque, covered with a whitish powder; an immature stage resembles scale insects; generally on plants, form a honeydew; plant pests, especially citrus and hothouse plants; life cycle somewhat complex: egg to active instar to scaly sessile instar to quiescent instar ("pupa") to last instar to adult.

Plant Lice (Superfamily Aphidoidea)—winged and wingless forms of both sexes; tarsi 2-segmented, with 2 claws; antennae long and hairlike; hind wings much smaller than fore wings; feed on plant sap, forming honeydew, some (ant cows) are herded and protected by ants; can be very harmful to many plants, would be more so except for parasitism by wasps and predation by lacewings, syrphid flies, and ladybird beetles; life cycle complex, highly

modified: fall eggs (may overwinter) to wingless stem mothers to wingless females to winged females (spring migrants) to summer wingless females to wingless or winged females to wingless or winged males and females (fall migrants) to eggs; migrant stages associated with movement from one plant host to another.

Scale Insects (Superfamily Coccoidea)—males with 1 pair of wings, females wingless; tarsi of 1 segment with 1 claw or legs absent, females may lack legs; antennae long to absent; feed on plant sap, often causing serious damage to plants; life cycle complex, highly modified: egg laid or young born alive to crawler (legs + antennae, active) to inactive stage (legs + antennae often lost, body with a waxy or scalelike covering) to inactive male stage ("pupa") and female adult under scale, males become adult and winged, eggs are fertilized.

Mealybugs (Superfamily Coccoidea)—males with or without 1 pair of wings (winged males resemble scale insect males), females wingless; tarsi of 1 segment with 1 claw, or legs absent; antennae long to absent; wingless forms covered by a white waxy secretion (no scale); feed on plant sap, often causing serious damage to plants; life cycle resembles that of scale insects.

SUBCLASS PTERYGOTA: DIVISION ENDOPTERYGOTA

Diagnosis: without bristlelike appendages on the underside of the abdomen; winged or from winged ancestors; life cycle characterized by complete metamorphosis, immature stages include larvae and pupae.

Order Neuroptera (Nerve-winged Insects)

Diagnosis: 4 wings, transparent and membranous, with many cross veins, roof the abdomen at rest; chewing mouthparts; freshwater or terrestrial; larvae and adults are insect predators; also preyed upon, especially by fish, hence a group copied for fishing "flies."

Fishflies (Family Corydalidae)—hind wings broader at base than fore wings; mouthparts (mandibles) inconspicuous; 4th tarsal segment cylindrical; flight fluttery; adults typically near fresh water, some attracted to lights; larvae (hellgrammites) freshwater, mostly under stream rocks.

Dobsonflies (Family Corydalidae)—hind wings broader at base than fore wings; mouthparts (mandibles) very long; 4th tarsal segment cylindrical; the largest species of fishfly, *Corydalus cornutus*, occurrence as in other fishflies.

Alderflies (Family Sialidae)—hind wings broader at base than fore wings; mouthparts (mandibles) inconspicuous; 4th tarsal segment inflated, deeply bilobed; adults typically near fresh water; larvae usually under rocks in streams.

Snakeflies (Suborder Raphidiodea)—wings similar in shape; wings with many veins; prothorax elongate; front

HOMOPTERANS

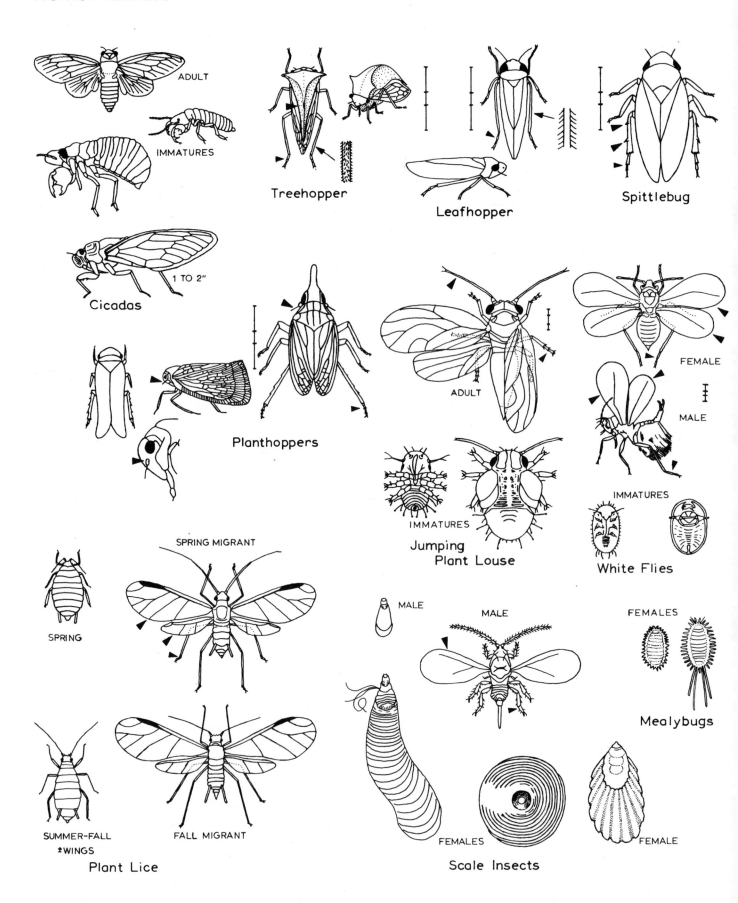

ADULT

IMMATURES

Treehopper

Leafhopper

Spittlebug

Cicadas

1 TO 2"

Planthoppers

ADULT

IMMATURES

Jumping
Plant Louse

FEMALE

MALE

IMMATURES

White Flies

SPRING MIGRANT

SPRING

SUMMER-FALL
±WINGS

FALL MIGRANT

Plant Lice

MALE

MALE

FEMALES

FEMALES

Mealybugs

FEMALE

Scale Insects

NERVE-WINGED INSECTS

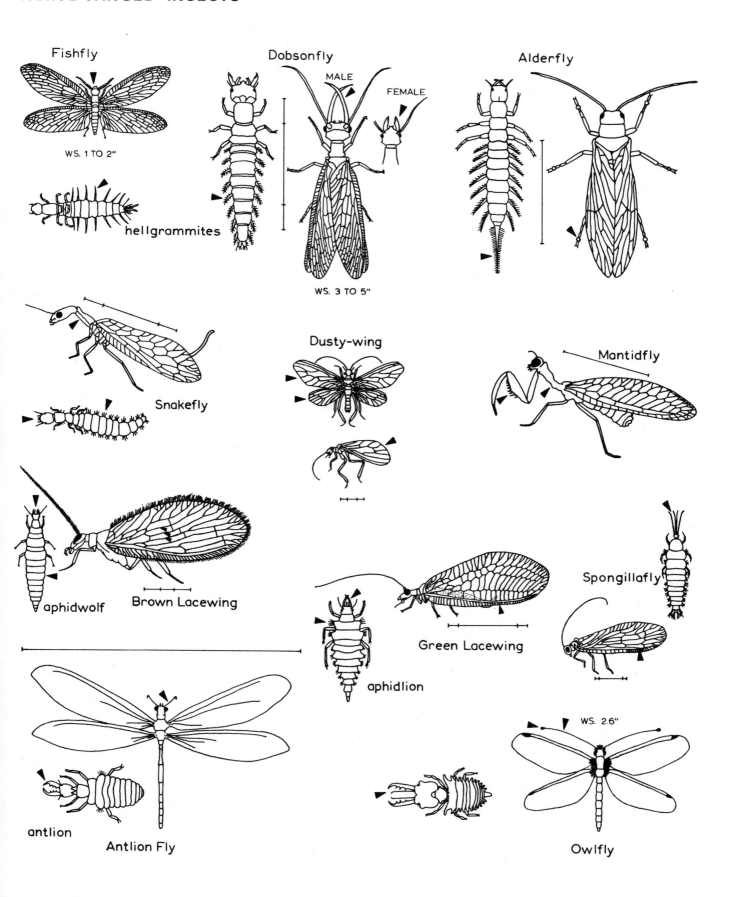

Fishfly
WS. 1 TO 2"

hellgrammites

Dobsonfly
MALE
FEMALE
WS. 3 TO 5"

Alderfly

Snakefly

Dusty-wing

Mantidfly

aphidwolf
Brown Lacewing

aphidlion
Green Lacewing

Spongillafly

antlion
Antlion Fly

WS. 2.6"
Owlfly

legs not raptorial; western states only; eggs and larvae generally under bark; adults terrestrial.

Dusty-Wings (Family Coniopterygidae)—wings similar in shape, with relatively few veins, covered with whitish powder; relatively rare, larvae and adults terrestrial.

Mantidflies (Family Mantispidae)—wings similar in shape, with many veins; prothorax elongate; front legs raptorial, resembling those of mantids; larvae parasitize spider egg sacs; adults terrestrial; metamorphosis more complex than in general case, 2 types of larvae.

Brown Lacewings (Family Hemerobiidae)—wings similar in shape, with many veins; prothorax of normal length; antennae hairlike, comblike, or like a string of beads, not clubbed or knobbed; brownish; unique wing venation; generally associated with plants; larvae (aphidwolves) and adults prey mostly on aphids or plant lice.

Green Lacewings (Family Chrysopidae)—wings similar in shape, with many veins; prothorax of normal length; antennae hairlike, comblike, or beadlike, not clubbed or knobbed; mostly green with yellow (coppery or goldish) eyes; often called stinkflies because of odor; unique wing venation; generally associated with plants; larvae (aphidlions) and adults prey mostly on aphids or plant lice.

Spongillaflies (Family Sisyridae)—wings similar in shape, with many veins; prothorax of normal length; antennae hairlike, comblike, or beadlike, not clubbed or knobbed; brownish; larvae freshwater, feeding on sponges, pupae in silk cocoons on objects near water, adults terrestrial; not commonly encountered, limited by freshwater sponges.

Antlion Flies (Family Myrmeleontidae)—wings similar in shape, with a great many veins; prothorax of normal length; antennae clubbed or knobbed; abdomen long and slender; resemble damselflies or dragonflies but antennae about as long as head plus thorax; larvae (antlions) construct conical pit in dry sand or dust, feeding upon arthropods falling into pit; adults poor fliers, terrestrial, attracted to lights.

Owlflies (Family Ascalaphidae)—wings similar in shape, with a great many veins; prothorax of normal length; antennae clubbed or knobbed, nearly as long as body; abdomen long and slender; resemble dragonflies except for long antennae; rare except for South and Southwest; larvae generally covered with debris, ambush small arthropods, especially insects.

Order Coleoptera (Beetles)

Diagnosis: most have 4 wings; front wings veinless, thick and leathery or horny, meeting along midline; hind wings sparsely veined and membranous, folded under front wings at rest; some females wingless; chewing mouthparts, sometimes on an elongate snout; number of tarsal segments (group of small segments at tip of each leg) often helpful in identification, number given in 3 parts indicating in proper order front-middle-hind leg segments; larvae wormlike, pupae rarely in a cocoon; very numerous, widespread, and with great variation in food habits; both beneficial and detrimental forms.

Wrinkled Bark Beetles (Family Rhysodidae)—body elongate, cylindrical; brownish or blackish; 3 longitudinal grooves on pronotum; antennae beadlike, 11 segments; tarsal segments 5-5-5; larvae and adults under bark; insect predators.

Tiger Beetles (Family Cicindelidae)—characteristic shape, elongate, cylindrical; usually brilliantly colored; head and eyes large; legs long and hairy; antennae hairlike, 11 segments; tarsal segments 5-5-5; larvae ground burrowers, lie in wait at surface opening, insect predators; adults in open sunny situations, often on sandy beaches, insect predators mostly.

Ground Beetles (Family Carabidae)—shape variable, often oval, most somewhat flattened; most dark and shiny, some colorful; typified by margined pronotum, large head and jaws, and hairlike antennae, 11 segments; tarsal segments 5-5-5; larvae under bark, in debris, burrowers under ground, insect predators; adults under objects or in open, run rapidly, seldom fly, insect predators.

Crawling Water Beetles (Family Haliplidae)—peculiar oval shape, convex; usually yellowish or brownish with black spots; 2 large plates on underside of abdomen; antennae hairlike, 11 segments; tarsal segments 5-5-5; adults and larvae freshwater herbivores, in or about water; adults swim or move slowly, often on plants.

Predaceous Diving Beetles (Family Dytiscidae)—characteristic streamlined, hard, smooth, oval body; blackish; hind legs paddlelike, fringed with long hairs; antennae hairlike, 11 segments; tarsal segments 5-5-5; predaceous, adult prey including small fish, larvae called water tigers; usually common in ponds and streams; adults often hang downward from water surface.

Whirligig Beetles (Family Gyrinidae)—oval flat; black or metallic green; 2nd and 3rd pairs of legs very short and flat, forelegs elongate and slender; antennae short, somewhat clubbed, 8 segments; tarsal segments 5-5-5; freshwater; predaceous, larvae often cannibalistic, adults prey mostly on insects dropping on water; often have fruity odor, observed whirling on ponds and quiet streams.

Hister Beetles (Family Histeridae)—broadly oval; usually shiny black; forewings short, squared-off, expose 1 or 2 abdominal segments; antennae elbowed, with a 3-segmented club, 11 segments; tarsal segments 5-5-5 or 5-5-4; larvae and adults usually on or around organic remains, also under bark and in ant nests; predaceous, mostly on scavenging insects.

Water Scavenger Beetles (Family Hydrophilidae)—oval, somewhat convex; usually black; palpi long, resembling antennae; antennae with a 4-segmented club, 7–10 segments; tarsal segments 5-5-5 or 5-5-4; most common in fresh water, some adults terrestrial on dung, some adults attracted to lights at night; larvae predaceous, adults scavengers.

Carrion Beetles (Family Silphidae)—body soft, somewhat flattened; forewings usually red and black and shorter than abdomen; antennae with a 4-segmented club or knob, 10–11 segments; tarsal segments 5-5-5; about ani-

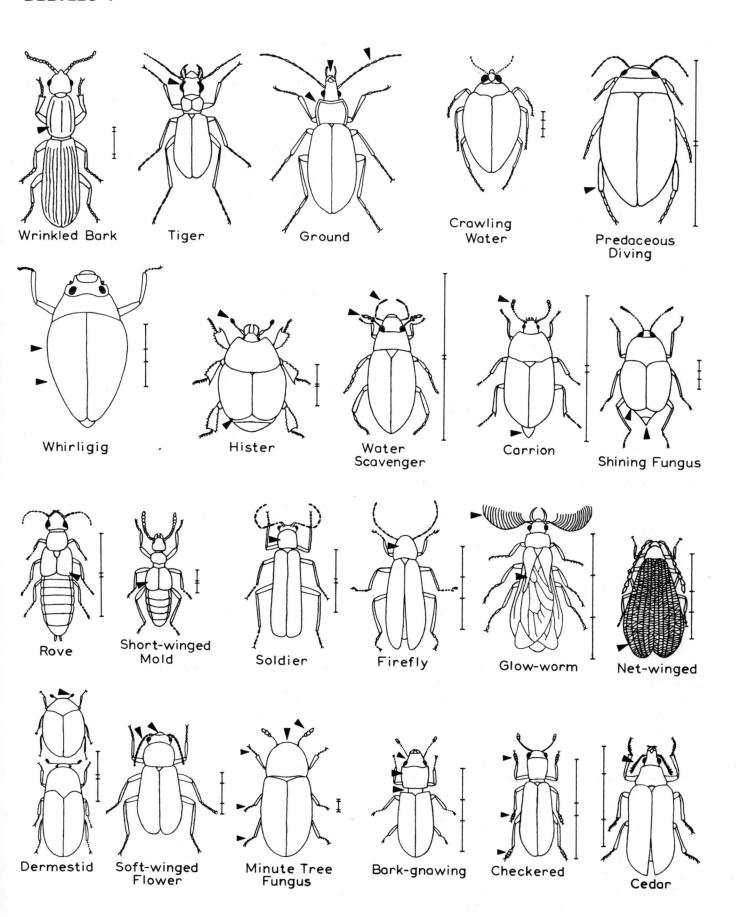

Wrinkled Bark

Tiger

Ground

Crawling Water

Predaceous Diving

Whirligig

Hister

Water Scavenger

Carrion

Shining Fungus

Rove

Short-winged Mold

Soldier

Firefly

Glow-worm

Net-winged

Dermestid

Soft-winged Flower

Minute Tree Fungus

Bark-gnawing

Checkered

Cedar

mal remains, rarely on fungi or in ant nests; mostly scavengers, many adults burying carrion by excavation from beneath (bury small rodents), some adults regurgitate food for their larvae, some adults predaceous on other scavengers.

Shining Fungus Beetles (Family Scaphidiidae)—pointed at each end, convex; shiny; head small, somewhat conical; fore wings shorter than pointed abdomen; antennae with a 5-segmented club; tarsal segments 5-5-5; in fungi, decaying plant matter and under bark.

Rove Beetles (Family Staphylinidae)—characteristic long and slender shape; black or colorful; wings usually very short; antennae usually clubbed, 9–11, usually 10, segments; tarsal segments 5-5-5, 4-5-5, 5-4-4, 4-4-4, 3-3-3, 2-2-2; active running and flying, usually about organic remains, also in ant nests; predators.

Short-Winged Mold Beetles (Family Pselaphidae)—resemble rove beetles but heavier-bodied; yellowish or brownish; antennae usually clubbed, 2–11 segments; tarsal segments 3-3-3 or 2-2-2, may seem 1-1-1; found under objects, among plant remains, in moss, and in termite or ant nests; predators.

Soldier Beetles (Family Cantharidae)—elongate and soft; often dark with colorful markings; resemble fireflies but pronotum (of typical shape and size) not covering head; antennae hairlike, 11 segments; tarsal segments 5-5-5; usually on flowers, often on lights at night; larvae predaceous; adults mostly predaceous on small insects including plant lice and mealybugs, also partly herbivorous.

Fireflies or Lightningbugs (Family Lampyridae)—elongate and very soft; color variable, dark and/or colorful; head concealed from above by typical pronotum; antennae hairlike, with sawtoothed edges, 11 segments; tarsal segments 5-5-5; usually found on plants; most adults do not feed, may possess a "tail light" which appears yellowish green even when not glowing; larvae predaceous.

Glow-Worms (Family Phengodidae)—most broad and flat; males with short fore wings and feathery, 12-segmented antennae; females larvalike; tarsal segments 5-5-5; found on plants or on the ground; larvae predaceous, adults may not eat.

Net-Winged Beetles (Family Lycidae)—fan-shaped; usually yellow or red with black markings; soft; forewings net-veined; antennae large, generally hairlike, 11 segments; tarsal segments 5-5-5; usually found in woody plant leaves and tree trunks; adults feed on plant juices, usually of decaying plants; larvae predaceous.

Dermestid or Skin Beetles (Family Dermestidae)—characteristic shape, oval, convex, usually densely haired or scaled; usually dark; antennae generally clubbed, short and fit into a groove, 5–11 segments; tarsal segments 5-5-5; found on organic remains, including leather and fur products; mostly scavengers, destructive, especially larvae.

Soft-Winged Flower Beetles (Family Melyridae)—elongate oval; most bright brown or red and black; many with peculiar orange-colored structures along sides of abdomen; antennae finely sawtoothed, 10–11 segments; tarsal segments 5-5-5; regularly found on flowers; mostly predaceous.

Minute Tree Fungus Beetles (Family Cisidae)—cylindrical; brownish to black; head bent down; resemble both bark beetles and branch and twig borers but tarsi 4-4-4 with segments 1–3 short, and antennal club of 3 segments; antennae with 3-segmented elongate club, 8–11 segments; found in dry woody fungi, decaying wood, or under bark; bore in wood, some attacking buildings and furniture; herbivorous.

Bark-Gnawing Beetles (Family Ostomidae)—elongate or oval; brownish, blackish, green, or blue; head and pronotum large, part behind pronotum waistlike; antennae with 3-segmented loose club, 11 segments; tarsal segments 5-5-5; found under logs and bark, in grain; omnivorous.

Checkered Beetles (Family Rhipiceridae)—elongate, convex; bright contrasting colors; body furry; palpi with terminal segment large; antennae usually clubbed or knobbed, sometimes hairlike, sawtoothed or comblike, 8–10 segments; tarsal segments lobed, 5-5-5; most found in or on logs or tree trunks, others on plants; predaceous, especially on wood-boring insects, a few feed upon pollen or prey upon bee and wasp nests.

Cedar Beetles (Family Rhipiceridae)—elongate oval, convex; brownish to black; antennal segments 2 or more times broader than long, 11 or rarely 12 segments; tarsal segments 5-5-5; one rare species in our area, under bark and logs in Florida.

Click Beetles (Family Elateridae)—elongate and flattened, usually parallel-sided and rounded at both ends; most brownish or blackish; rear corners of pronotum usually with a point or spine; with a joint, clicking apparatus, between bases of front 2 legs; antennae usually with sawtoothed edges, also hairlike or comblike, 11 or rarely 12 segments; tarsal segments 5-5-5; found on plants and under bark; larvae ("wireworms") and adults mostly herbivorous, larvae destructive to farm crop seeds, some larvae insect predators.

False Click Beetles (Family Eucnemidae)—resemble click beetles; most brownish; head bent down; pronotum somewhat rectangular, distinctly convex above; click poorly; antennae fit into grooves; antennae beadlike, hairlike, sawtoothed, or comblike, 11 segments; tarsal segments 5-5-5; occur in wood starting to decay, especially maple and beech; adults regularly quiver antennae.

Pseudo Click Beetles (Family Throscidae)—resemble click beetles, oblong; brownish or blackish; head bent down; mouthparts hidden; pronotum essentially trapezoidal in shape; clicking apparatus fused together, do not click; antennae sawtoothed or with a loose, 3-segmented club, 11 segments; tarsal segments 5-5-5; found mostly on flowers, especially of dogwood, milkweed and mayapple.

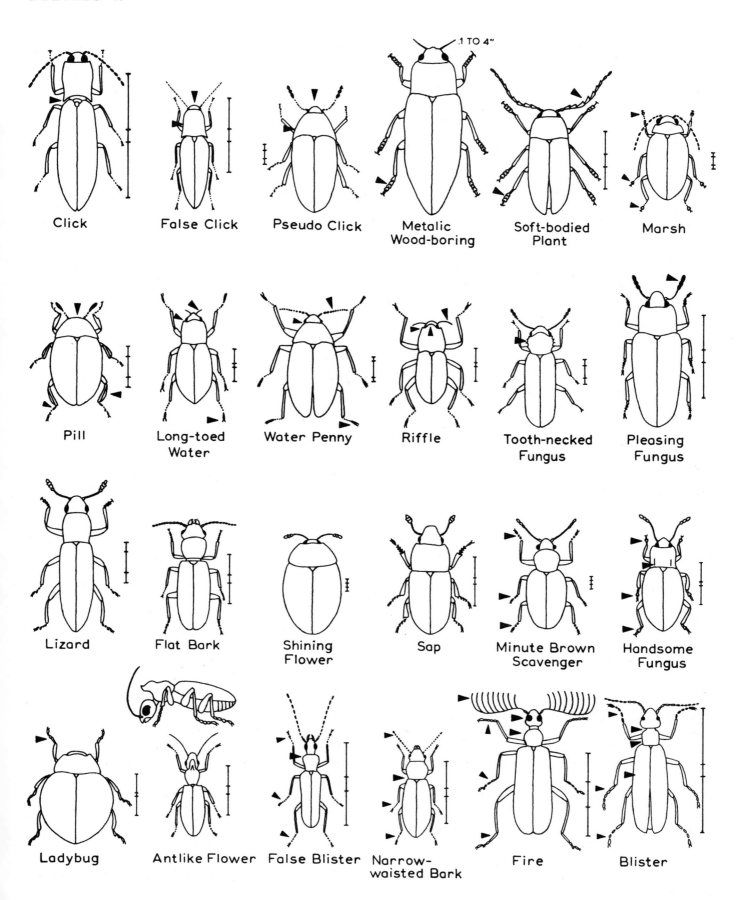

.1 TO 4"

Click

False Click

Pseudo Click

Metalic
Wood-boring

Soft-bodied
Plant

Marsh

Pill

Long-toed
Water

Water Penny

Riffle

Tooth-necked
Fungus

Pleasing
Fungus

Lizard

Flat Bark

Shining
Flower

Sap

Minute Brown
Scavenger

Handsome
Fungus

Ladybug

Antlike Flower

False Blister

Narrow-
waisted Bark

Fire

Blister

Metallic Wood-Boring Beetles (Family Buprestidae)—characteristic compact shape, hard-boiled; usually metallic-colored; head bent down; antennae usually sawtoothed, 11 segments; tarsi with some segments bilobed, 5-5-5; found on dying and dead trees, tree remains and leaves of living woody plants; larvae bore in living, dying, or dead wood.

Soft-Bodied Plant Beetles (Family Dascillidae)—elongate to short and broad, soft-bodied, hairy; brownish, often mottled; antennae sawtoothed, comblike, or with tongue-like lobes, 11 segments; tarsi with segments 2–4 strongly bilobed beneath, 5-5-5; mostly in plants in moist areas.

Marsh Beetles (Family Helodidae)—oval, convex; pale to dark; a longitudinal keel or ridge below each eye; antennae hairlike or sawtoothed, 1st segment large, 11 segments; tarsi with segment 4 only lobed, 5-5-5; adults in moist debris and marshy areas, larvae in fresh water.

Pill Beetles (Family Byrrhidae)—oval, convex; gray to brown to black, also green; head bent down, hidden from above; hind femora large, extend to margin of forewing; tibia usually flattened and expanded; antennae hairlike to clubbed, 11 segments; tarsi with last segment longest, 5-5-5 or 4-4-4; occur in sandy areas, often under objects; draw up legs and become motionless when disturbed.

Long-Toed Water Beetles (Family Dryopidae)—oval to elongate, convex; finely haired; dull gray to brown; head partly covered by prothorax; antennae short, hairlike, finely haired, 11 segments; tarsi with last segment plus claws longer than segments 1–4, 5-5-5; usually seen crawling on stream bottoms or flying near streams.

Water Penny Beetles (Family Psephenidae)—oval, convex, flattened; gray, dark brown, or black; head partly covered by prothorax; antennae moderately long, sawtoothed, 11 segments; tarsi with last segment plus claws longer than segments 1–4, 5-5-5; on plants bordering streams; larvae, called water pennies, flat and broadly elliptical (almost circular), under stream and pond shore objects.

Riffle or Drive Beetles (Family Elmidae)—elongate, cylindrical but somewhat flattened; color brownish; head partly covered by prothorax, prothorax expanded in front; antennae fairly short, slender, hairlike, last segment longest, 11 segments; tarsal segments 5-5-5; under stones or debris in stream riffles.

Tooth-Necked Fungus Beetles (Family Derodontidae)—oval to elongate, convex; brownish; sometimes mottled; pronotum toothed; fore wings with rows of square punctures or polished rough spots; under decaying bark in fungi.

Pleasing Fungus Beetles (Family Erotylidae)—hemispherical to elongate-oval; shiny, usually black with reddish yellow markings; larger forms black with 2 orange-red transverse bands on fore wings; many resemble darkling beetles; antennae short with a 3-5, usually 3-, segmented club, 11 segments; tarsal segments 5-5-5, often appearing as 4-4-4; under dead bark, in fungi, in sap.

Lizard Beetles (Family Languriidae)—long and narrow, cylindrical but slightly flattened; black with reddish pronotum; antennae with a 4-segmented club, 11 segments; tarsal segments 5-5-5, may seem 4-4-4; on plants; herbivorous, many larvae are stem borers.

Flat Bark Beetles (Family Cucujidae)—elongate, usually extremely flattened; yellowish, reddish, or brownish; antennae with a 2-4 segmented club, or hairlike, 11 segments; tarsal segments 5-5-5, some seem 5-5-4; under bark of newly cut trees, in stored grain (flat grain beetles); mostly predaceous, on mites and small insects, some larvae insect parasites.

Shining Flower Beetles (Family Phalacridae)—oval, convex; usually brownish, shiny; antennae with a 3-segment, elongate, oval club, 11 segments; tarsal segments 5-5-5, appear to be 4-4-4; on flowers, especially composites.

Sap Beetles (Family Nitidulidae)—Usually oval, also elongate, somewhat flattened; pale to brownish, often with red or yellow markings; tip of abdomen may be exposed by short wings; antennae with a 3-segment club, 11 segments; tarsal segments 5-5-5 or 4-4-4; most in fermenting plant juices, also in flowers, near carrion, and under bark of dead trees.

Minute Brown Scavenger Beetles (Family Lathridiidae)—elongate oval, somewhat convex; reddish brown or brownish; each fore wing with 6–8 rows of punctures; antennae with a 2- or 3-segment elongate club or knob, 8–11 segments; tarsal segments 3-3-3, 2-3-3 or 2-2-3; in flowers, debris or molds.

Handsome Fungus Beetles (Family Endomychidae)—oval to elongate-oval; brownish with pale or reddish markings; may resemble ladybugs; head clearly visible from above; 2 longitudinal grooves on pronotum; antennae with a loose, 3-segment club, 8–11 segments; tarsal segments 4-4-4, most seem 3-3-3; near fungi in decaying wood and debris; feed on fungi, especially molds.

Ladybugs or Ladybird Beetles (Family Coccinellidae)—round to oval, rarely oblong, convex; usually red or black, variously marked or spotted; antennae with a 3–6 segment club; tarsi 4-4-4, seem 3-3-3; on plants, generally seeking aphids, predaceous.

Antlike Flower Beetles (Family Anthicidae)—generally antlike in appearance; head bent down and strongly constricted behind the eyes; antennae generally hairlike or beadlike, 11 segments; on plants and under objects, some under or on ground debris.

False Blister Beetles (Family Oedemeridae)—elongate, slender, somewhat flattened, transversely convex; color from pale to brownish, often with red, orange, yellow, or blue markings; soft-bodied; pronotum broadened anteriorly; antennae hairlike, rarely sawtoothed, 11 segments, rarely appear as 12; tarsal segments 5-5-5, may seem 4-4-3, 3rd and rarely 2nd bilobed or heart-shaped; adults on plants, attracted to night lights; larvae in moist, decaying wood, often in driftwood.

Narrow-Waisted Bark Beetles (Family Salpingidae)—elongate to heavy-bodied, may be somewhat flattened; dark-colored; resemble ground beetles but pronotum narrow at rear and poorly or not margined; head occasionally snoutlike; antennae usually clubbed, sometimes with sawtoothed edges, 11 segments; tarsi 5-5-4; under bark, debris and rocks, on plants; predaceous.

Fire Beetles (Family Pyrochroidae)—flattened; black with yellow to red thorax, yellowish hairs over body; eyes frequently large; head and pronotum narrow; fore wings broadened posteriorly; antennae sawtoothed, comblike, or somewhat featherlike, 11 segments; adults on plants and under bark; larvae under dead tree bark.

Blister Beetles (Family Meloidae)—most elongate; color variable, frequently bright; soft-bodied; head bent down; neck narrow; pronotum narrower than head or fore wings; fore wings soft and flexible; antennae essentially hairlike or beadlike, 11, rarely 8 or 9, segments; tarsi 5-5-4; most on plants; predaceous, most larvae feed on grasshopper eggs, a few larvae live in bee nests, feeding on bee eggs and food; larval stages include differently appearing larvae; body fluids contain chemical that causes skin blisters.

Tumbling Flower Beetles (Family Mordellidae)—characteristic streamlined conformation, body wedge-shaped, head bent down, hump-backed, wings shorter than pointed abdomen; color variable, usually some combination of black, red, yellow, and white; antennae short, generally hairlike or sawtoothed, 11 segments; tarsal segments 5-5-4; adults active, running and flying insects, on plants; often tumble to escape; larvae in plant tissues or decaying wood.

Comb-Clawed Beetles (Family Alleculidae)—elongate-oval, somewhat flattened; brownish to blackish; hairy; claws with comblike inner margin; antennae hairlike, somewhat sawtoothed, or rarely comblike, 11 segments; tarsal segments 5-5-4; adults on plants, on or in fungi; larvae mostly in organic remains of wood, herbs, or fungi.

Darkling Beetles (Family Tenebrionidae)—shape variable, often elongate and convex; usually black, often brownish, sometimes with red or white marks; eyes usually notched; antennae hairlike or beadlike but usually somewhat clubbed, sometimes sawtoothed, 11, rarely 10, segments; tarsal segments 5-5-4; adults common in drier climates, under objects, under bark, on plants, in grain, around lights at night; mostly herbivorous; when disturbed, some elevate abdomen, exuding fluid having a foul odor.

Long-Jointed Bark Beetle (Family Lagriidae)—elongate, cylindrical, somewhat flattened; dark metallic blue, green, or reddish; antennae hairlike, occasionally somewhat sawtoothed, last segment elongate, 11 segments; tarsal segments 5-5-4; adults mostly on leaves, also under dead bark or logs, on plants; larvae under bark or plant debris.

False Darkling Beetle (Family Melandryidae)—elongate-oval, convex, partially flattened; mostly brown or dark; marks near edge of pronotum; antennae hairlike, sometimes thickened or sawtoothed, 11, rarely 10, segments; tarsal segments 5-5-4; most under dead bark or logs, also on plants.

Spider Beetles (Family Ptinidae)—vaguely spiderlike, elongate-oval to convex; brownish, often with white patches; head and pronotum much narrower than fore wings; legs elongate; antennae hairlike, usually 11 segments, also 2 or 3; tarsal segments 5-5-5; in museum collections, old wood and stored products.

Deathwatch Beetles (Family Anobiidae)—cylindrical to oval to somewhat globular; color brownish, rarely with white or pale markings; head bent down, not visible from above; legs short, contractile; antennae frequently with last 3 segments elongate, may be slightly to markedly comblike, 11 segments; tarsal segments 5-5-5; mostly in dry plant matter, grain, bark, twigs, branches; includes drugstore beetles which infest drugs and cereals.

Branch and Twig Borers or Powder Post Beetles (Family Bostrichidae)—elongate, compact, somewhat cylindrical; usually black, rarely red with black markings; head bent down, not visible from above; pronotum shape distinctive, pebbled and rasplike; antennae not elbowed, with a 3–4 segment club, 8–10 segments; tarsal segments 5-5-5; wood borers in living trees, most in dry plant material, also under bark, in grain; includes western short circuit beetle, normally bores in trees, also into lead covering of telephone cables.

Branch and Twig Borers or Powder Post Beetles (Family Psoidae)—like Bostrichidae except head clearly visible from above and generally smaller; bore in living or dead trees.

Powder Post Beetles (Family Lyctidae)—elongate, slender, somewhat flattened; brown to reddish brown; head exposed, narrows behind eyes; antennae with a 2-, rarely 3-, segment club, 11 segments; tarsal segments 5-5-5, may seem 4-4-4; boring exposes powder in dry wood.

Stag Beetles or Pinchingbugs (Family Lucanidae)—somewhat elongate and flattened, convex; brownish to blackish; jaws large, some branched, resembling stag antlers; antennae like scarab beetles but are elbowed and terminal segments cannot be held together in a compact club, 4 segments clublike or comblike, 10 segments; tarsal segments 5-5-5; adults in woods, attracted to lights; larvae in decaying wood; herbivorous and scavengers.

Bessybugs or Peg or Bess Beetles (Family Passalidae)—elongate, cylindrical, somewhat flattened; black; scarablike, but fore wings with longitudinal grooves and head with a "horn;" antennae with a 3-segment, comblike club that can be closed into a somewhat tight knob, 10 segments; tarsal segments 5-5-5; form colonies in decaying wood.

Scarab Beetles (Family Scarabaeidae)—heavy-bodied, oval to elongate, convex; variably colored, often bright; antennae with 3-7, usually 3, platelike segments forming a club, 7–11, usually 10, segments; tarsal segments 5-5-5

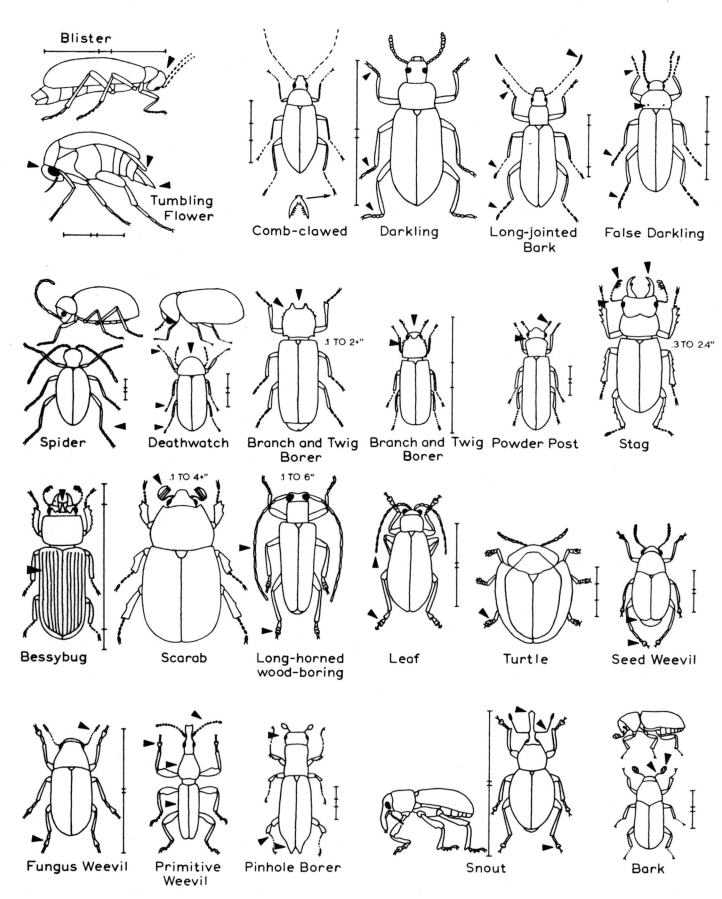

Blister

Tumbling Flower

Comb-clawed

Darkling

Long-jointed Bark

False Darkling

Spider

Deathwatch

Branch and Twig Borer

Branch and Twig Borer

Powder Post

Stag

.1 TO 2+"

.3 TO 2.4"

Bessybug

Scarab

Long-horned wood-boring

Leaf

Turtle

Seed Weevil

.1 TO 4+"

.1 TO 6"

Fungus Weevil

Primitive Weevil

Pinhole Borer

Snout

Bark

or 0-5-5; mostly scavengers on trees, logs and plants, under bark and logs; many nocturnal and attracted to lights.

Long-Horned Wood-Boring or Long-Horned Beetles (Family Cerambycidae)—variable, most elongate and cylindrical, but to oval and flat; variably colored, generally brownish, often bright; may resemble leaf beetles; most over 1/2 inch long; most with inner eye margins notched; antennae usually at least half body length, 11, rarely 10, or 12–25 or more segments; tarsal segments 5-5-5, appear 4-4-4 with 3rd bilobed and 4th hidden in notch of 3rd; wood boring, on trees, logs and other plants, under bark and logs, many nocturnal.

Leaf Beetles (Family Chrysomelidae)—variable, elongate and cylindrical to oval and flat; variably colored, often bright; may resemble long-horned wood-boring beetles; almost always under 1/2 inch long; antennae usually much less than 1/2 body length, hairlike, sawtoothed, sometimes with terminal segment enlarged, 11, rarely less, segments; tarsal segments 5-5-5, appear 4-4-4, like those of long-horned wood-boring beetles; on plants, especially bindweeds or morning glories; generally herbivorous.

Turtle Beetles (Family Chrysomelidae)—somewhat turtlelike, other features like those of leaf beetles.

Seed or Bean Weevils (Family Bruchidae)—compact, usually oval, to oblong or squarish; dull grayish, brownish, blackish, or black; head small, usually with a short snout; front wings not covering abdomen tip; antennae sawtoothed, comblike or clubbed, 11 segments; tarsi like long-horned wood-boring and leaf beetles, 5-5-4; in stored seeds.

Fungus Weevils (Family Anthribidae)—elongate, flattened to oval, convex, some mitelike; usually brownish, with white to gray to black markings; beak short and broad; antennae not elbowed, of moderate length, and with a 3-segment club, or as long as those of many long-horned wood-boring beetles, then club may be absent, 11 segments; tarsal segments 4-4-4, may seem 3-3-3; in dead twigs, under dead bark.

Primitive or Straight-Snouted Weevils (Family Brentidae)—long and narrow, two sides of body almost parallel, cylindrical; reddish with brownish markings or brownish; snout straight, long and slender, to short and blunt; prothorax almost as long as fore wings; antennae beadlike or hairlike, not elbowed, 10–11 segments; tarsal segments 5-5-5, may seem 4-4-4; under loose bark, larvae wood boring.

Pinhole Borers (Family Platypodidae)—elongate, slender, cylindrical; pale to dark brown; head broad, erect, wider than pronotum; fore wings elongate, shape distinctive; antennae with a large unsegmented club, 5–7 segments; tarsal segments 5-5-5, 1st segment longer than rest combined; bore in living trees.

Snout Beetles or Weevils (Family Curculionidae)—considerable shape variation, often somewhat egg-shaped in outline; color variable, often blackish or brownish, some-times very colorful; snout usually distinctive, usually long; antennae usually elbowed and arising from snout, 1st segment elongate, 3-segment club, 9–11 segments; tarsal segments 5-5-5, seem 4-4-4; bore in plants.

Bark or Engraver Beetles (Family Scolytidae)—includes ambrosia and timber beetles; very stout to somewhat elongate, cylindrical; usually brownish or blackish; antennae elbowed with a large, solid, club, 3–10 segments; large spine or projection at apex of front tibia; tarsal segments 5-5-5, appear as 4-4-4; mine under bark of living or dead trees.

Order Strepsiptera (Twisted-winged Insects)

Diagnosis: males with tiny front wings and fan-shaped, few-veined, membranous hind wings; females wingless and without eyes or antennae; chewing mouthparts; extremely complex life cycle: females and larvae entirely parasitic on other insects, hosts showing distorted abdomens and perhaps protruding strepsipteran, males sometimes free-living and under rocks; rarely encountered.

Order Mecoptera (Scorpionflies)

Diagnosis: 4 slender, membranous, many-veined wings, roof abdomen at rest, reduced in some males and absent in some females; chewing mouthparts on a distinctive downward-extending beak; some males curve the abdomen end upward, scorpionlike; mostly on plants, some found in snow; scavengers, herbivores or carnivores.

Snow Scorpionflies (Family Boreidae)—tarsi with 2 claws; male wings bristlelike, females wingless; dark-colored; usually found in and feed upon moss, often encountered on winter snow.

Earwig Scorpionflies (Family Meropeidae)—tarsi with 1 claw; wings present, short and broad; male abdomen terminated by pincers, resemble those of earwigs; very rare, 1 known species known from lights and under rocks in East.

Scorpionflies (Family Panorpidae)—tarsi with 1 claw; wings present, long and narrow; male genitalia (end of abdomen) resemble scorpion stingers; on plants, mostly scavengers, also eat fruits and nectar.

Hanging Scorpionflies or Hangflies (Family Bittacidae)—tarsi with 1 claw; winged or wingless; very long-legged, hang by forelegs from leaves or twigs; on plants, small insect and spider predators.

Order Trichoptera (Caddisflies)

Diagnosis: 4 membranous, mostly longitudinally veined wings, roof abdomen at rest; body and wings haired or scaled; mouth parts vestigial; antennae long and hairlike; larvae freshwater, often in rapid water, usually case-making and clinging to underside of rocks; case of sand, debris, or plant matter; larvae scavengers or predators; adults poor fliers, usually close to streams, feed upon liquids.

Twisted-winged Insects

Snow Scorpionfly

Scorpionfly

Hanging Scorpionfly

±WINGS

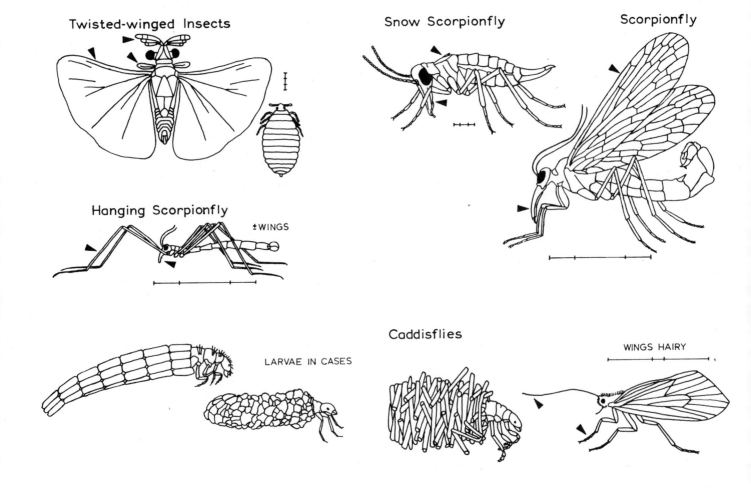

LARVAE IN CASES

Caddisflies

WINGS HAIRY

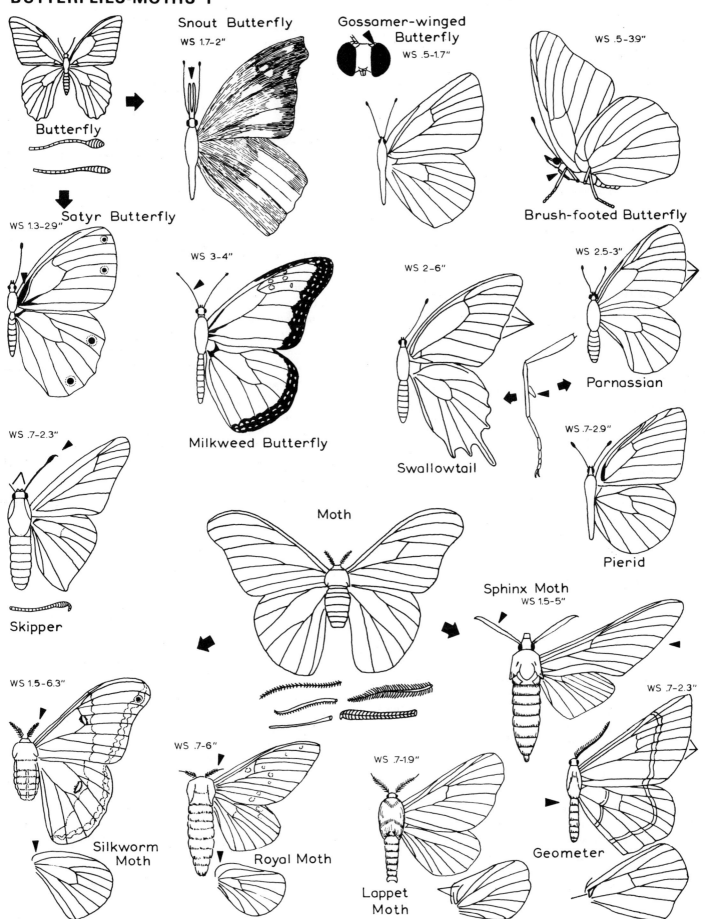

Butterfly

Snout Butterfly
WS 1.7–2"

Gossamer-winged Butterfly
WS .5–1.7"

WS .5–3.9"

Satyr Butterfly

Brush-footed Butterfly

WS 1.3–2.9"

WS 3–4"

WS 2–6"

WS 2.5–3"

Parnassian

WS .7–2.9"

Milkweed Butterfly

Swallowtail

Pierid

WS .7–2.3"

Skipper

Moth

Sphinx Moth
WS 1.5–5"

WS .7–2.3"

WS 1.5–6.3"

WS .7–6"

WS .7–1.9"

Silkworm Moth

Royal Moth

Lappet Moth

Geometer

Order Lepidoptera (Butterflies, Skippers and Moths)

Diagnosis: 4 membranous wings (rarely reduced or absent in some females), covered with overlapping scales, held horizontally to vertically at rest; larvae mouthparts chewing, adults, sucking; larvae are wormlike caterpillars, with 2 silk glands on mouthpart for spinning pupal stage cocoon; larvae herbivorous, often destructive to plants, or scavengers that may harm clothing and stored grain; adults feed upon liquids, especially plant nectar, include valuable plant pollinators.

Butterflies (Suborder Frenatae, part)

Diagnosis: fore and hind wings unlike in shape and venation, antennae threadlike and knobbed at tip.

Snout Butterflies (Family Libytheidae)—palpi as long or longer than thorax; generally brownish; rare; larvae feed on hackberry.

Gossamer-Winged Butterflies (Family Lycaenidae)—eyes slightly notched or indented at antennae; face width between eyes much less than length; includes metalmarks (usually with metallic spots), hairstreaks (usually with hairlike tails), elfins (usually brownish and with scalloped rear margins of hind wings), coppers (most reddish or brownish with a coppery luster), harvesters (brown with large orangish blotch in center of each wing, wingspread about 1 inch), blues (small and usually blue); larvae sluglike, many secrete "honeydew," some live in ant nests.

Brush-Footed Butterflies (Family Nymphalidae)—1st pair of legs without claws and less than half the length of 2nd and 3rd pair, held folded up against thorax (some slight reduction in 1st legs is also found in satyrs, snout butterflies, and milkweed butterflies—check their unique features); the largest family of butterflies; includes fritillaries (generally brownish with many black markings, usually dots and/or wavy lines), checkerspots (dark, often black with small yellow to orange bars and/or blotches), crescents (resemble checkerspots but with a pale crescent on underneath outer margins of hind wings); angelwings (sharp angular wing margins), buckeyes (large eyespot on top surface of each hind wing), thistle butterflies (variously marked but with white spots or blotches confined to apex of fore wings), tortoise shells (wing margins scalloped, resembling angelwings but front wing rear margin straight instead of concave), admirals (irregular white band continuous from front margin of fore wing to rear margin of hind wing), viceroys (wings reddish or orangish brown with black veins and margins, black margins with white marks alternating with veins), red-spotted purples (with metallic green in hind wings), leafwing butterflies (underside of wings resemble dead leaves), emperor butterflies (orangish to brownish with light and dark markings including subcircular dark spots alternating with veins near upper margins of hind wings), purple wings (usually dull purplish above), dagger wings (elongate tails resembling

swallowtails but with prolonged tips to fore wings), and tropic queens (orange or dark with dark margins and white marks including irregular bar at tip of fore wing and irregular arc just below bar); larvae feed on various plants.

Satyr Butterflies (Family Satyridae)—fore wing with at least 1 main vein swollen at the base; generally dull-colored, often with eyespots on upper and lower surfaces of wings; larvae feed upon grasses.

Milkweed Butterflies (Family Danaidae)—antennae completely free of scales; brownish or orangish brown; 2 species, the widespread monarch which has dark lines along the veins, and the southeastern states queen which lacks a black border to the veins; larvae of both species feed upon milkweed; monarch is one of few migratory butterflies, over 1800 mile flights verified.

Swallowtails (Family Papilionidae)—1st pair of legs with a movable pad or lobelike process on inner surface of tibia; unique venation; either tailed *or* not yellowish or white; larvae feed on a variety of plants.

Parnassians (Family Papilionidae)—1st pair of legs with a movable pad or lobelike process on inner surface of tibia; unique venation; no tails; white or yellowish with dark markings; larvae feed on plants.

Pierids (Family Pieridae)—possess none of the above butterflies' characteristics; tarsal claws forked or divided into 2 parts; includes whites, sulfurs, dog-faces, marbles (orange tip with green marbling on underside of hind wings), orange tips; larvae feed mostly on mustards and legumes.

Skippers (Suborder Frenatae, part)

Diagnosis: fore and hind wings unlike in shape and venation; antennae widely separated at base and usually drawn out and hooked at the tip; stout-bodied.

Giant Skippers (Family Megathymidae)—antennae not hooked at tip; wingspread 1.5 or more inches; larvae in plant stems and roots, generally yucca.

Skippers (Family Hesperiidae)—antennae hooked at tip or not; wingspread 1.2 or less inches; larvae feed on plants, usually from inside a leaf shelter, also surround cocoon with leaves.

Frenate Moths (Suborder Frenatae, part)

Diagnosis: fore and hind wings unlike in shape and venation; antennae generally not clubbed, if clubbed a spine or group of spines present at point where front margin of hind wing inserts into the body.

Sphinx or Hawk Moths (Family Sphingidae)—antennae thickened, spindle-shaped, often hooked at tip; heavy-bodied; narrow-winged; mostly nocturnal, also diurnal; rapid fliers, flight and feeding often resembles hummingbirds; most larvae with a hornlike process near end of abdomen, called hornworms.

Giant Silkworm Moths (Family Saturnidae)—antennae feathery (males) or comblike on each side (females);

heavy-bodied; wings often wide, hairy and soft-scaled, not white, many bright and/or conspicuously colored, usually with transparent windows and/or eyespots; front base of hind wing only slightly expanded; larvae feed mostly on tree and shrub leaves.

Royal Moths (Family Citheroniidae)—antennae feathery but not to tip; heavy-bodied; wings often wide, hairy, and soft-scaled, not white, many bright and/or conspicuously colored, without eyespots; front base of hind wing greatly expanded; larvae feed on trees.

Lappet Moths and Tent Caterpillars (Family Lasiocampidae)—unique venation; stout-bodied; hairy; antennae feathery; larvae make silken "tents" or "mats" on woody plants and feed upon leaves.

Geometers and Measuring Worms (Family Geometridae)—unique venation resembles prominents; bodies slender, fragile-appearing; wings delicate but generally broad, often marked with light or dark wavy lines; legs not covered with long hairs; larvae, measuring worms, loop body when crawling, includes a group causing serious damage by defoliating deciduous, including orchard, trees.

Prominents (Family Notodontidae)—unique venation resembles geometers; bodies heavy, hairy; at least upper part of legs covered with long hairs; usually brownish or yellowish, wings sometimes lined; antennae usually simple, rarely feathery in males; larvae feed upon trees and shrubs, sometimes orchard pests.

Tiger and Footman Moths (Family Arctidae)—unique venation resembles noctuids, foresters, and tussocks; wings white, yellow, or brightly spotted or banded (footmen small, slender, mostly dull-colored); antennae hairlike, thickened or feathery; larvae feed on trees, shrubs and herbs, sometimes doing serious damage.

Noctuids (Family Noctuidae in Broad Sense)—unique venation resembles tigers, footmen, foresters, and tussocks; mostly dull-colored, some with brightly colored hind wings; larvae found on all parts of all types of plants, contribute to much farm crop damage.

Forester Moths (Family Agaristidae)—unique venation resembles tigers, footmen, noctuids, and tussocks but antennae thickened at tip; usually black with 2 whitish to yellowish spots in each wing; larvae frequently defoliate grapes and Virginia creeper.

Tussock Moths (Family Liparidae)—unique venation resembles tigers, footmen, noctuids, and foresters; mostly dull-colored with or without markings; feed mostly on trees, can cause serious forest damage.

Wasp Moths and Ctenuchas (Family Amatidae)—unique venation; often wasplike but not as much so as clearwings; ctenuchas are dark except for yellow, orange, or red on thorax and/or head (some have pigment superimposed on veins); larvae mostly on herbs; adults day-flying.

Microlepidoptera

Diagnosis: hind wings either with 3 anal veins or a fringe of hairs as wide or wider than wings.

Casebearers (Family Coleophoridae)—wings very narrow, sharply pointed, rear margins fringed with scales; head smooth; usually pale in color; larvae start as leaf miners, then form cases (of leaves and excrement held with silk) which they carry while skeletonizing leaves, spend winter in case.

Clothes Moths (Family Tineidae)—wings very narrow, often pointed, hind margins fringed with scales; head roughened by hairs and scales; grayish to brown or iridescent; larvae scavengers, important destroyers of dry animal products, especially fabrics.

Diamondback Moths (Family Plutellidae)—wings very narrow, fore wings sometimes sickle-shaped, hind margins fringed with scales; head smooth or roughened; antennae directed forward; fore wings when folding show 3 diamond-shaped marks on inner margins; larvae start as leaf miners, changing to leaf surface feeders, mostly on mustard family.

Bagworm Moths (Family Psychidae)—males with well-developed wings, scaled or nearly scaleless, and relatively large bodies; females and larvae live in a silk bag having attached bits of leaves, feed on tree leaves.

Ermine Moths (Family Yponomeutidae)—wings rather broad, margin rounded; hind wings approximate size of fore wings, lance-shaped or with a short fringe; usually bright-colored; larvae mostly leaf feeders.

Clearwing Moths (Family Aegeriidae)—many wasp- or beelike; wings narrow, partly devoid of scales, so partly transparent; dark blue or black, marked with yellow or red, often iridescent; larvae borers, mostly in woody parts of woody plants.

Gelechiid Moths (Family Gelechiidae)—wings narrow; hind wings generally broader than fore wing and outer margin curved with apex pointed; larvae form galls or mine in most parts of a variety of plants.

Smoky Moths (Family Pyromorphidae)—wings long, narrow, and thinly scaled; antennae slender and feathery; coloration gray to black (smoky), often marked yellow or red; larvae skeletonize leaves, often of grapes or Virginia creeper.

Leafrollers (Family Olethreutidae)—wings tend to be square-tipped; most can be recognized by the fringe of long hairs arising from base of a hind wing vein; coloration gray, tan, or brown, often banded or mottled, rarely metallic; larvae feed on tree and vine leaves, also bore in growing branch tips; leaf feeders generally roll and join leaves with silk.

Bell Moths (Family Tortricidae)—wings square-tipped, held rooflike over body at rest providing bell-shaped outline; coloration gray, tan, or brown, mottled or spotted; larvae secure a rolled leaf retreat with silk, drop via silk line from retreat when disturbed, climb back to retreat via silk line; larvae generally leaf feeders.

Carpenter and Leopard Moths (Family Cossidae)—fore wings often large, spotted (leopard) or mottled (carpenter); coloration pale gray to brown; heavy-bodied; re-

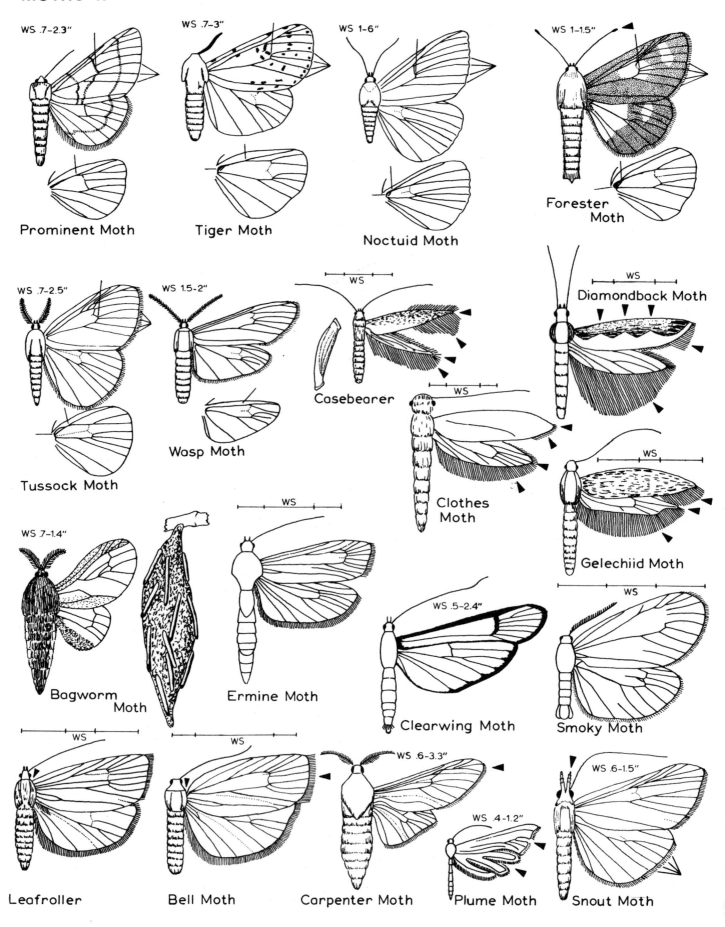

WS .7-2.3"

Prominent Moth

WS .7-3"

Tiger Moth

WS 1-6"

Noctuid Moth

WS 1-1.5"

Forester Moth

WS .7-2.5"

Tussock Moth

WS 1.5-2"

Wasp Moth

WS

Casebearer

WS

Clothes Moth

WS

Diamondback Moth

WS

Gelechiid Moth

WS .7-1.4"

Bagworm Moth

WS

Ermine Moth

WS .5-2.4"

Clearwing Moth

WS

Smoky Moth

WS

Leafroller

WS

Bell Moth

WS .6-3.3"

Carpenter Moth

WS .4-1.2"

Plume Moth

WS .6-1.5"

Snout Moth

semble sphinx moths but lack long, coiled mouth parts; larvae bore in wood.

Snout Moths (Family Pyralidae)—fore wings triangular or elongate, hind wings with typical venation; labial palps often project to form a snout; coloration tan to brown; larvae on plants, organic remains, or in fresh water

Plume Moths (Family Pterophoridae)—wings split lengthwise, margins fringed with scales; larvae borers or leaf rollers.

Jugate Moths (Suborder Jugatae)

Diagnosis: wings similar in venation and often shape; rare.

Order Diptera (Flies)

Diagnosis: 2 membranous wings or none, hind wings represented by short, knobbed structures; piercing-sucking or sponging mouthparts, often drawn out; very numerous, widespread; larvae wormlike, called maggots; many pests and truly dangerous species, larvae often ruin meat, mosquitoes carry malaria and other diseases; varied food habits, many scavengers and insect predators.

Crane Flies (Superfamily Tipuloidea)—body, wings, and especially legs, long and slender; V-shaped suture on top of thorax (mesonotum) between wings; larvae in moist soil or organic remains to fresh water, scavengers or herbivores, some economic plant pests; adults widespread, generally associated with moisture.

Moth or Sand Flies (Family Psychodidae)—typical shape, mothlike; usually very hairy; larvae in organic remains and water; adults in shady, often moist areas, especially in sewers, drains, organic remains; some blood-sucking.

Net-Winged Midges (Family Blephariceridae)—resemble crane flies; wings sometimes with netlike lines, hind margins near body projecting; uncommon; larvae on rocks in swift streams, adults nearby.

Mosquitoes (Family Culicidae)—resemble crane flies; wings with scales along veins; head with long snout; larvae aquatic, feeding on microorganisms; adults widespread, generally near water, blood-sucking.

Gall Midges or Gall Gnats (Family Cecidomyiidae)—characteristic gnat shape; long antennae; typical venation; most larvae form plant galls, others in fungi, in plant remains, or under bark; mostly herbivores, some predators, insect parasites, or scavengers.

March Flies (Family Bibionidae)—stout-bodied; short antennae; typical venation; larvae feed on roots and decaying plants; adults generally found on flowers.

Buffalo Gnats or Black Flies (Family Simuliidae)—robust, hump-backed; short antennae; broad wings, typical venation; larvae on rocks or other objects in swift streams, feed on microorganisms; adults widespread but generally near streams; females vicious biters, blood-sucking, large groups can kill livestock, especially numerous at times in coniferous forests, generally in high mountains.

Gnats (Families Anisopodidae, Mycetophilidae, and Sciaridae)—characteristic gnat shape; long antennae; typical venation; larvae generally in moist places, soil, fungi, organic remains, and plants, mostly scavengers or herbivores; adults normally near larvae.

Biting Midges, No-See-Ums, or Punkies (Family Ceratopogonidae)—unique venation, wings generally with dark pattern; larvae in fresh water or saturated sand, mud, or organic debris, rare intertidally, probably scavengers; adults generally near water, blood-sucking, serious biting pests, also predators.

Midges (Families Dixidae, Chaoboridae, and Chironomidae)—mosquitolike but wings without scales; unique venation; larvae in fresh water, surface feeders on algae or predators, especially on mosquito larvae, rarely scavengers in moist land situations, under bark, in organic remains; adults do not bite, often swarm.

Soldier Flies (Family Stratiomyidae)—variable except for unique wing venation; most dark-colored, often with light markings, many brightly colored; abdomen wasplike to flat and broad; larvae widespread, generally freshwater or moist land situations; adults widespread.

Horse Flies (Family Tabanidae)—robust; venation shared with deer flies; 3rd antennal segment not elongate; larvae generally freshwater predators; adults generally near larvae, females blood-sucking, pests.

Deer Flies (Family Tabanidae)—venation shared with horse flies; 3rd antennal segment elongate; typically with dark wing patterns; larvae generally freshwater predators; adults generally near larvae, females blood-sucking, pests.

Snipe Flies (Family Rhagionidae)—typical body shape; unique venation, wings may have dark patterns; larvae in moist remains or debris, generally in woods, predators; adults in woods, predators.

Stiletto Flies (Family Therevidae)—typical shape; unique venation; larvae in soil or debris, predators; adults uncommon, usually in open areas, predators.

Robber Flies (Family Asilidae)—unique body shape and venation; larvae in debris, wood, or soil, predators; adults widespread, highly predaceous, especially on larger insects, capture prey on wing, bite is painful.

Bee Flies (Family Bombyliidae)—most robust and hairy with long proboscis and pigmented wings, often resemble bees, especially in habits; unique venation; larvae insect parasites or predators; adults frequently around flowers, active on warm, sunny days, often hover.

Dance Flies (Family Empididae)—most with a large thorax and slender abdomen; typical venation; larvae in soil, under bark, in debris, or in fresh water; adults swarm, move up and down ("dance"), widespread, usually near moisture and plants.

Long-Legged Flies (Family Dolichopodidae)—usually metallic red, green, or blue; male genitalia folded under abdomen; legs relatively long; unique venation; larvae in grass stems, under bark, in decaying wood, and in mud,

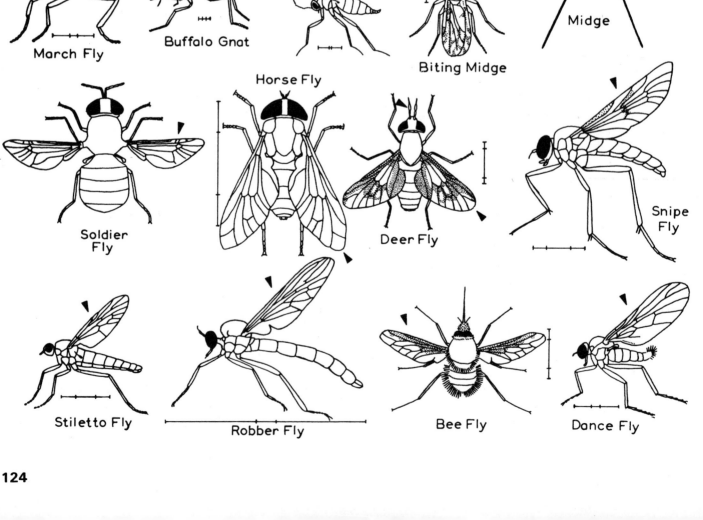

Crane Fly

Moth Fly

Net-winged Midge

Mosquito

Gall Midge

Gnat

Biting Midge

Midge

March Fly

Buffalo Gnat

Soldier Fly

Horse Fly

Deer Fly

Snipe Fly

Stiletto Fly

Robber Fly

Bee Fly

Dance Fly

predators; adults widespread, generally moist areas, predators.

Flower Flies (Family Syrphidae)—many beelike; unique venation; larvae widespread, including ant, wasp, bee, and termite nests, predators; adults widespread, generally around flowers, hover, pollinate flowers, feed on nectar, tree sap, and fruit juices.

Hump-Backed Flies (Family Phoridae)—strongly humpbacked; hind femora flattened; unique venation; larvae widespread, including ant and termite nests, predators and parasites; adults widespread, especially about plant remains, scavengers.

Big-Headed Flies (Family Pipunculidae)—large heads, especially eyes; uncommon; larvae parasitic, mostly on plant bugs, leaf hoppers.

Picture-Winged Flies (Families Richardiidae, Otitidae, and Platystomatidae)—bodies generally metallic-colored; wings with yellowish, brownish, or black patterns; typical venation; larvae mostly in organic remains; adults generally on plants.

Fruit or Peacock Flies (Family Tephritidae)—wings often spotted or banded brown or black; eyes iridescent green; unique wing venation; larvae generally leaf miners, gall formers, or borers, include very serious agricultural pests; adults generally about plants.

Vinegar or Pomace Flies (Family Drosophilidae)—generally yellowish; unique venation; larvae generally about decaying plant matter; adults normally near larvae; the "fruit" flies used in the study of heredity.

Grass or Frit Flies (Family Chloropidae)—yellowish to dark, body relatively bare; unique venation; larvae mostly scavengers, also gall formers or borers, in grasses; adults common about grass.

Leaf-Miner Flies (Family Agromyzidae)—unique venation; larvae leaf miners; adults widespread.

Muscid Flies (Family Muscidae)—unique venation; larvae scavengers in organic remains and dung, also feed on plants; adults widespread; includes many well-known flies, house, stable, horn, face, and tsetse.

Horse Bot Flies (Family Gasterophilidae)—robust, hairy, often resemble bees; female abdomen elongate, pointed and folded under; larvae hatch on or near host's lips, or when lips of host (horse, mule, or donkey) remove eggs from their attachment on host, larvae become intestinal parasites; adults about larval hosts.

Dung Flies (Family Anthomyiidae)—unique venation; larvae often scavengers in dung or organic remains, also feed on plants; adults widespread, often near larvae.

Louse Flies (Family Hippoboscidae)—most wingless, resembling sucking lice; parasites on birds and mammals; winged forms mostly bird parasites.

Blow Flies (Family Calliphoridae)—resemble muscids but most are metallic blue or green (include bluebottle and greenbottle flies); unique venation; larvae mostly flesh scavengers, also in wounds of mammals; adults widespread, mostly scavengers.

Flesh Flies (Family Sarcophagidae)—resemble muscids; red eyes; typical antennae; 3 stripes on thorax; larvae mostly scavengers in mammal skin or wounds, also arthropod parasites; adults widespread, mostly scavengers.

Tachinid or Tachina Flies (Family Tachinidae)—resemble muscids; typical antennae; larvae internal parasites of insects; adults widespread.

Robust Bot Flies (Family Cuterebridae)—large, robust, hairy, beelike; head generally unique; larvae parasitic, forming warbles on rodents; adults fairly rare.

Warble or Bot Flies (Family Oestridae)—robust, hairy, beelike; head generally unique; larvae animal parasites, migrating through host's body to tissues infested, especially sheep, goats, cattle, rarely on man; adults may fly 50 m.p.h.

Order Siphonaptera (Fleas)

Diagnosis: wingless; antennae short, thick, clubbed, partially hidden in grooves; body laterally compressed; legs specialized for jumping; mouthparts sucking; adults periodic external parasites of birds and mammals, bloodsucking; transmit such truly dangerous diseases as bubonic plague and typhus fever to man.

Order Hymenoptera (Sawflies, Horntails, Wasps, Bees, and Ants)

Diagnosis: 4 membranous wings or none, relatively few veins, wings on each side interlocking via hooks during flight, variously held at rest; chewing or chewing-lapping mouthparts; egg-laying apparatus (ovipositor) of female modified for sawing, piercing, or stinging; larvae wormlike, sometimes legless; pupae typically in cocoons; very numerous, include all social insects (bees, wasps, and ants) except termites; social insects have different types of individuals (castes) performing different functions within a colony of their species, e.g., see yellow jackets and bumble bees; widespread, in various habitats; feeding habits variable; perhaps most beneficial order of insects, includes many insect parasites and predators, plant pollinators, and the honey bee.

Sawflies (Superfamily Tenthredinoidea)—abdomen broadly joined to thorax; body more-or-less heavy, usually dark or colorful; larvae generally on trees, leaf feeders, some very destructive forest insects; adults generally about trees, solitary.

Horntails (Superfamily Siricoidea)—abdomen broadly joined to thorax, terminated by a horny, spearlike spine; dark or brilliant and metallic; larvae have horns, wood borers in various trees, often destructive; adults generally about trees, females bore in trees to deposit eggs, frequently die owing to inability to remove ovipositor, solitary.

Stem Sawflies (Family Cephoidea)—abdomen broadly joined to thorax; body slender, compressed; frequently black with yellow or other markings; larvae borers in

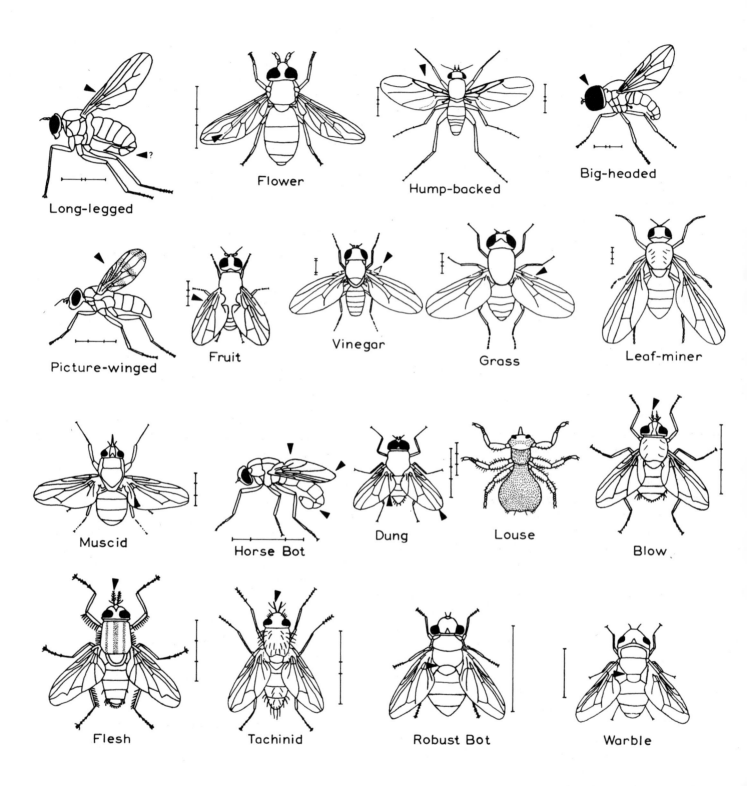

Long-legged

Flower

Hump-backed

Big-headed

Picture-winged

Fruit

Vinegar

Grass

Leaf-miner

Muscid

Horse Bot

Dung

Louse

Blow

Flesh

Tachinid

Robust Bot

Warble

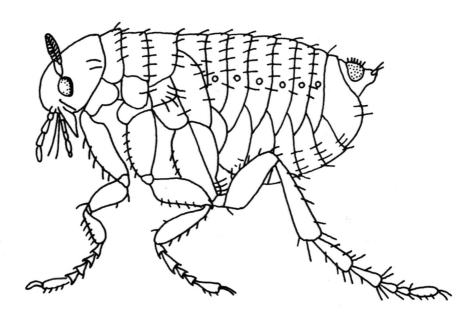

berries and grasses, possibly destructive to cereals; adults generally about grassy areas; solitary.

Braconid Wasps (Family Braconidae)—abdomen narrowly joined to thorax, waistlike; antennae straight, with 12, usually 16, or more segments; front wings with well-developed venation and a dark spot near front margin but without a vein directly from spot to base of wing; unique wing venation; abdomen not greatly elongate; larvae insect parasites, often of insects destructive to forests; adults often about flowers; solitary.

Ichneumon Wasps (Family Ichneumonidae)—abdomen narrowly joined to thorax, waistlike; antennae straight, with 16 or more segments; front wings with well-developed venation and a dark spot near front margin but without a vein directly from spot to base of wing; unique wing venation; abdomen elongate, curved; larvae insect parasites, often of insects destructive to forests; adults widespread, often about lights at night; solitary.

Gallwasps (Superfamily Cynipoidea)—mostly minute; abdomen narrowly joined to thorax, waistlike; flealike or compressed laterally; wing venation unique, reduced; most black; abdomen generally shiny; larvae plant feeders, gall-forming; egg, larva, and pupa stages spent in plant tissues, emerge as adults; adults generally about plants; solitary.

Chalcid Wasps (Superfamily Chalcidoidea)—mostly minute; abdomen narrowly joined to thorax, waistlike; body shape and possible wing venations (reduced) typical; antennae tend to be elbowed; larvae mostly insect (egg and larva) parasites, parasitic mostly on destructive forms; adults widespread, generally common plants; solitary.

Ensign Wasps (Family Evaniidae)—abdomen narrowly joined to thorax, waistlike; typical body shape, vaguely spiderlike; unique wing venation; black; larvae roach egg parasites; adults near roaches, generally buildings; solitary.

False Ichneumon Wasps (Family Gasteruptiidae)—abdomen narrowly joined to thorax, waistlike; resemble ichneumon wasps but hind wing sparsely veined; typically blackish or black with reddish abdomen; larvae parasitize wasps, bees, and wood-boring beetles; adults uncommon, generally found on flowers; solitary.

Long-Tailed Wasps (Family Pelecinidae)—abdomen narrowly joined to thorax, waistlike; male rare, with short abdomen, female with extremely long abdomen; shining black; larvae parasitic on scarab beetles; solitary.

Proctotrupoid Wasps (Superfamily Proctotrupoidea, part)—abdomen narrowly joined to thorax, waistlike; typical shape; wings veinless or hind wing with 1 typical vein; larvae insect and spider parasites; adults generally encountered about plants, may ride adult of host; solitary.

Cuckoo, Jewel, or Gold Wasps (Family Chrysididae)—abdomen narrowly joined to thorax, waistlike; body usually sculptured; metallic green or blue; abdomen with 3 or 4 segments visible from above and hollowed underneath; unique venation; larvae external parasites of adult bees and wasps; adults subject to attack by hosts, secretive in laying eggs in host nests, roll in ball when disturbed; solitary.

Tiphiid Wasps (Family Tiphiidae)—abdomen narrowly joined to thorax, waistlike; typical thoracic structure, pronotum essentially triangular in side view; moderately hairy, usually black, some black and yellow; legs short; larvae parasitic on larvae of tiger beetles, scarab beetles, bees, and wasps; some females wingless, females burrow to host larva site; solitary.

Velvet Ants (Family Mutillidae)—abdomen narrowly joined to thorax, waistlike; typical thoracic structure, pronotum essentially triangular in side view; males winged, females wingless; densely hairy; usually brightly colored with yellow, orange, or red markings; larvae external insect parasites, especially of bees, wasps, flies, and beetles; females frequently encountered during active movement on open ground, males often carry wingless female into air during mating; solitary.

Scoliid or Hairy Flower Wasps (Family Scoliidae)—abdomen narrowly joined to thorax, waistlike; typical thoracic structure, pronotum essentially triangular in side view; resemble male velvet ants, hairy with 1 or more yellow bands on abdomen but wing membrane beyond cells is finely wrinkled; larvae external parasites of scarab beetle larvae; adults generally encountered about flowers; solitary.

Ants (Family Formicidae)—abdomen narrowly joined to thorax, waistlike; typical thoracic structure, pronotum essentially triangular in side view; waist with 1 or 2 segments, each with a node; mostly wingless; social insects with 3 castes, queens (reproductives) winged prior to reproductive flight, kings (reproductives) winged prior to reproductive flight (both reproductives shed wings after flight), and workers (sterile, wingless females); reproductives produced seasonally; colonial (10 to thousands per colony); colonies within a wide variety of places, especially herbs, shrubs, trees, and ground; eggs, larvae, and pupae in colony; adults within and about colony, seeking a wide variety of food.

Spider Wasps (Family Pompilidae)—abdomen narrowly joined to thorax, waistlike; typical thoracic structure, pronotum essentially triangular in side view; legs long, spiny; most dark with yellowish, orangish, or darkish (smoky) wings, some are bright-colored; larvae feed upon spiders; adults generally found on ground or plants, form nests in soil burrows, in cracks or holes in buildings, trees or rocks, in spider nests, and in mud cells, stock nests with spiders; solitary.

Yellowjackets or Hornets (Family Vespidae, Subfamily Vespinae)—abdomen narrowly joined to thorax, waistlike; typical thoracic structure, pronotum essentially triangular in side view; wing venation producing typical cell; wings folded longitudinally at rest; apex of middle tibia with 2 spines or spurs; tarsal claws simple; larvae feed on insects in nests; nests of many paper cells enclosed in a

paper covering (paper formed by wasps by chewing leaves and wood); nests hanging from projecting surfaces (e.g., of trees and buildings) or underground; social insects with queens (only caste surviving winter, start new colonies each spring), kings or males, and workers (sterile females), queens and workers can give potent sting.

Potter or Mason Wasps (Family Vespidae, Subfamily Eumeninae)—abdomen narrowly joined to thorax, waistlike; typical thoracic structure, pronotum essentially triangular in side view; wing venation producing typical cell; apex of middle tibia with 1 spine or spur; mandibles knifelike, elongate, often crossing one another; tarsal claws toothed or forked; larvae in potlike mud nest, feed on caterpillars or bettle larvae provided by female wasp at time of egg-laying; mud nests in abandoned wasp nests, in log or tree cavities, or in underground burrows; solitary wasps.

Paper Wasps (Family Vespidae, Subfamilies Polistinae and Polybiinae)—abdomen narrowly joined to thorax, waistlike; typical thoracic structure, pronotum essentially triangular in side view; wing venation producing typical cell; apex of middle tibia with 2 spines or spurs; tarsal claws simple; hind wing with a lobe near base of rear margin; larvae feed on insects in nests; nests usually a single comb of paper cells, no covering; nests hanging by a paper stalk from projecting surfaces of trees or buildings, cavities in logs or trees, or burrows or holes in the ground; some make mud or clay nests in like sites; social or solitary.

Solitary Vespid Wasps (Family Vespidae, Subfamilies Euparagiinae, Masarinae, and Zethinae)—abdomen narrowly joined to thorax, waistlike; typical thoracic structure, pronotum essentially triangular in side view; wing venation producing typical cell; apex of middle tibia with 1 spine or spur; tarsal claws simple; larvae are fed insects in nests; nests variable, generally sand or mud on twigs or rocks; solitary, some approach social forms because many females share a single nest of cemented plant materials.

Ampulicid Wasps (Family Ampulicidae)—abdomen narrowly joined to thorax, waistlike; typical thoracic structure, pronotum with a rounded lobe; unique appearance, pronotum elongate with a conical, anterior extension; larvae provided immature cockroaches in nests, nests under ground debris, under bark, or in twigs; relatively rare; solitary.

Varicolored Wasps (Family Sphecidae, Subfamily Astatinae)—abdomen narrowly joined to thorax, waistlike; typical thoracic structure, pronotum with a rounded lobe; body heavy, black or black with red abdomen; fore wing marginal cell squared off at end and with a short appended vein; nest in ground, larvae are fed true bugs; adults generally about flowers; solitary.

Sand-Loving Wasps (Family Sphecidae, Subfamily Larrinae)—abdomen narrowly joined to thorax, waistlike; typical thoracic structure, pronotum with a rounded lobe; dull-colored; fore wing marginal cell not squared off at end

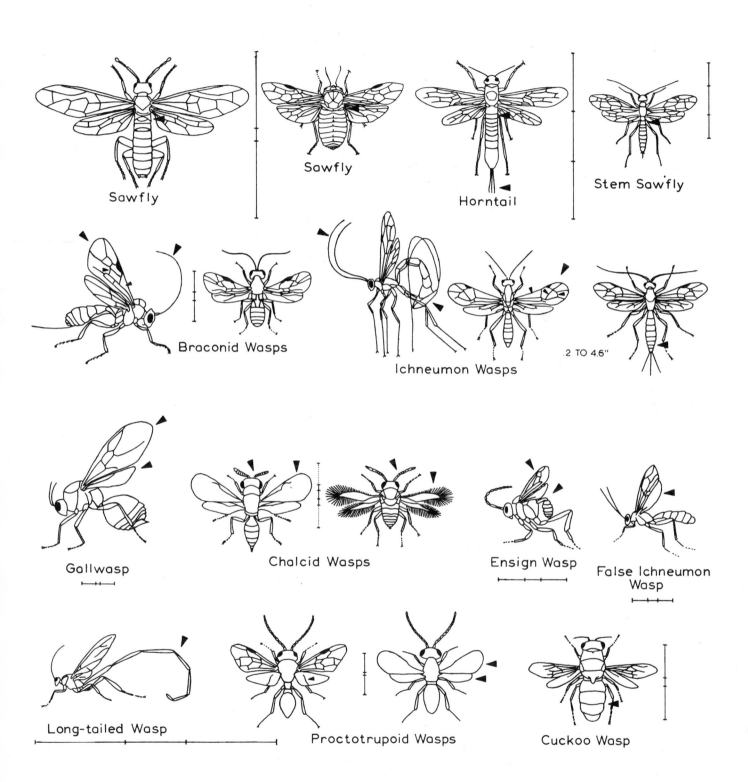

Sawfly

Sawfly

Horntail

Stem Sawfly

Braconid Wasps

Ichneumon Wasps

.2 TO 4.6"

Gallwasp

Chalcid Wasps

Ensign Wasp

False Ichneumon Wasp

Long-tailed Wasp

Proctotrupoid Wasps

Cuckoo Wasp

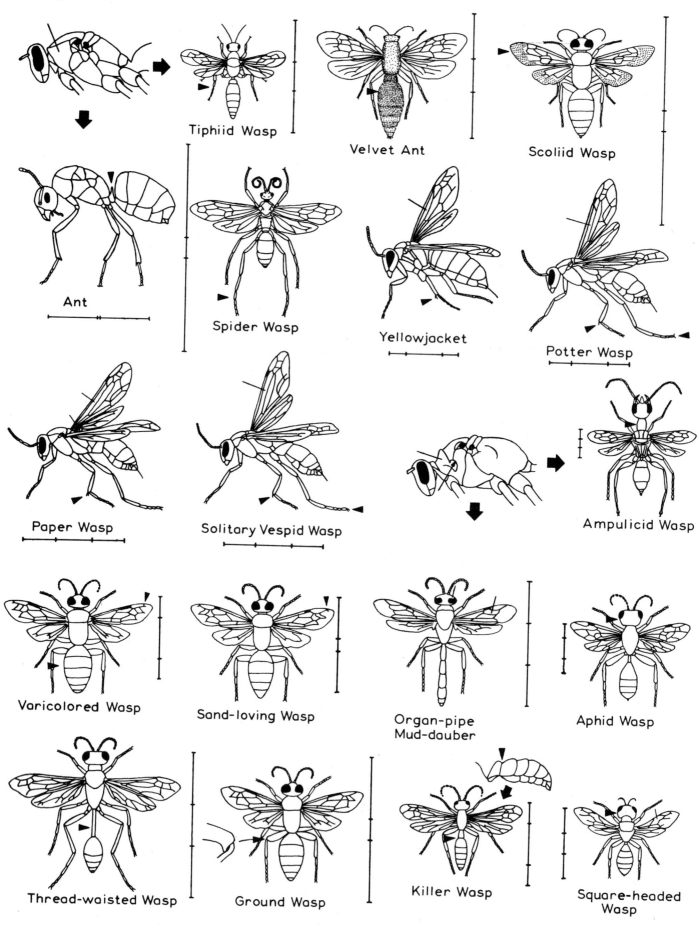

Tiphiid Wasp

Velvet Ant

Scoliid Wasp

Ant

Spider Wasp

Yellowjacket

Potter Wasp

Paper Wasp

Solitary Vespid Wasp

Ampulicid Wasp

Varicolored Wasp

Sand-loving Wasp

Organ-pipe
Mud-dauber

Aphid Wasp

Thread-waisted Wasp

Ground Wasp

Killer Wasp

Square-headed
Wasp

but with a short appended vein; most nest in burrows in sand, larvae are fed spiders, true bugs, grasshoppers, and crickets; adults generally about flowers; solitary.

Organ-Pipe Mud-Daubers (Family Sphecidae, Subfamily Trypoxyloninae)—abdomen narrowly joined to thorax, waistlike; typical thoracic structure, pronotum with a rounded lobe; elongate, usually shining black; inner margin of eyes deeply notched; generally make mud nests, individual nest cells often joined so as to resemble organ pipes; male guarding nest during female's absence, others nest in cavities; larvae fed spiders; adults generally about flowers; solitary.

Aphid Wasps (Family Sphecidae, Subfamily Pemphredoninae)—abdomen narrowly joined to thorax, waistlike; typical thoracic structure, pronotum with a rounded lobe; head large, body slender, usually black; nests in tree or ground cavities; larvae fed true bugs, aphids, and hoppers; adults generally about flowers; solitary.

Thread-Waisted Wasps (Family Sphecidae, Subfamily Sphecinae)—abdomen narrowly joined to thorax, waistlike; typical thoracic structure, pronotum with a rounded lobe; body slender, waist more-or-less elongate; usually black with yellow or orange on abdomen; many nest in ground burrows; larvae fed caterpillars, crickets or grasshoppers; includes mud-daubers which feed larvae spiders in mud nests; adults common, generally about flowers; solitary.

Ground Wasps (Family Sphecidae, Subfamily Nyssoninae)—abdomen narrowly joined to thorax, waistlike; typical thoracic structure, pronotum with a rounded lobe; undersurface of apex of hind tibia with a flattened extension; nest in ground burrows; larvae fed butterflies, flies, cicadas, hoppers, wasps, bees, and grasshoppers; adults generally about flowers, also farm animals; solitary.

Killer Wasps (Family Sphecidae, Subfamily Philanthinae)—abdomen narrowly joined to thorax, waistlike; typical thoracic structure, pronotum with a rounded lobe; side view of abdomen discloses a distinct dorsal notch between 1st and 2nd segments; usually black with yellow markings; nest in ground burrows; larvae fed beetles, bees, or winged ants; adults generally about flowers; solitary.

Square-Headed Wasps (Family Sphecidae, Subfamily Crabroninae)—abdomen narrowly joined to thorax, waistlike; typical thoracic structure, pronotum with a rounded lobe; head large, squarish, typical sphecid vein absent; usually black with yellow markings; nest in ground burrows or existing chambers in wood; larvae fed flies; adults generally about flowers; solitary.

Mining Bees (Family Andrenidae)—some body hairs, generally including those on thorax, branched or feathery; 2 lines, sutures, below each antennal socket; pronotum like sphecid wasps; nest in ground burrows, a single entrance giving rise to branching tunnels, an egg or larva at each end; larvae fed on pollen and honey; widespread, generally on flowers; solitary but many nests usually close together, often in open areas.

Plasterer Bees (Family Colletidae, Subfamily Colletinae)—some body hairs, generally including those on thorax, branched or feathery; pronotum like sphecid wasps; 1st segment of hind tarsus elongate, usually flattened or thickened, frequently hairy; lobe on rear margin of hind wing longer than cell adjacent to rear margin; unique venation; includes 3 submarginal cells; nest in ground burrows or various natural cavities, line with gelatinous material, plaster; larvae fed pollen and honey; widespread, generally on flowers; solitary.

Yellow-Faced Bees (Family Colletidae, Subfamily Hylaeinae)—some body hairs, generally including those on thorax, branched or feathery; pronotum like sphecid wasps; 1st segment of hind tarsus elongate, usually flattened or thickened, frequently hairy; lobe on rear margin of hind wing longer than cell adjacent to rear margin; unique venation, includes 2 submarginal cells; face usually with yellow markings; nest in ground burrows or various natural cavities; larvae fed pollen and honey; widespread, generally on flowers; solitary.

Sweat Bees (Family Halictidae)—some body hairs, generally including those on thorax, branched or feathery; pronotum like sphecid wasps; 1st segment of hind tarsus elongate, usually flattened or thickened, frequently hairy; lobe on rear margin of hind wing longer than cell adjacent to rear margin; unique venation, includes 3 submarginal cells; basal vein strongly arched; nests resemble those of mining bees but a single entrance may serve several bees; larvae fed pollen and honey; widespread, generally on flowers; tend to alight on perspiring humans; solitary.

False Sweat Bees (Family Melittidae)—some body hairs, generally including those on thorax, branched or feathery; pronotum like sphecid wasps; first segment of hind tarsus elongate, usually flattened or thickened, frequently hairy; lobe on rear margin of hind wing shorter than cell adjacent to rear margin; some with 2 submarginals as in leafcutting bees, others with 3 submarginal cells as other bees that are diagnosed after leafcutters, but neither as stout nor as hairy as leafcutting bees; nests resemble those of mining bees; larvae fed pollen and honey; widespread, generally on flowers; solitary.

Leafcutting Bees (Family Megachilidae)—some body hairs, generally including those on thorax, branched or feathery; pronotum like sphecid wasps; 1st segment of hind tarsus elongate, usually flattened or thickened, frequently hairy; lobe on rear margin of hind wing shorter than cell adjacent to rear margin; 2 submarginal cells a character found elsewhere only in yellow-faced and false sweat bees; body stout, abdomen hairy; nests generally in natural cavities, lined with cut pieces of leaves; some lay eggs in the nests of other bees; larvae fed pollen and honey; widespread, generally about flowers; nesting solitary or parasitic.

Cuckoo Bees (Family Apidae, Subfamily Anthophorinae)—some body hairs, generally including those on thorax, branched or feathery; pronotum like sphecid wasps; 1st segment of hind tarsus elongate, usually flattened or thick-

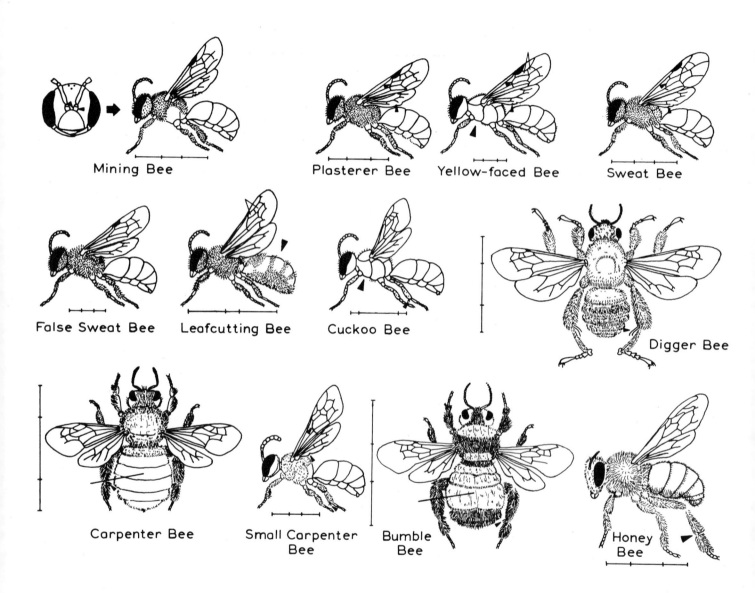

Mining Bee

Plasterer Bee

Yellow-faced Bee

Sweat Bee

False Sweat Bee

Leafcutting Bee

Cuckoo Bee

Digger Bee

Carpenter Bee

Small Carpenter Bee

Bumble Bee

Honey Bee

ened; frequently hairy; apex of hind tibia with 2 spurs; body sparsely haired; eggs laid in the nests of other bees; larvae fed pollen and honey; widespread; nesting parasitic.

Digger Bees (Family Apidae, Subfamily Anthophorinae)— some body hairs, generally including those on thorax, branched or feathery; pronotum like sphecid wasps; 1st segment of hind tarsus elongate, usually flattened or thickened, frequently hairy; apex of hind tibia with 2 spurs; body hairy, including back of abdomen but without color pattern of bumble bees; nest in ground, cells lined with wax; larvae fed pollen and honey; widespread, generally about flowers; solitary.

Carpenter Bees (Family Apidae, Subfamily Xylocopinae, Xylocopa)—some body hairs, generally including those on thorax, branched or feathery; pronotum like sphecid wasps; 1st segment of hind tarsus elongate, usually flattened or thickened, frequently hairy; apex of hind tibia with 2 spurs; body hairy but top of abdomen bare, color pattern often resembles bumble bees; nests excavated in wood; larvae feed upon honey and pollen; widespread, generally about flowers or dead wood; solitary.

Small Carpenter Bees (Family Apidae, Subfamily Xylocopinae, Ceratina)—some body hairs, generally including those on thorax, branched or feathery; pronotum like sphecid wasps; 1st segment of hind tarsus elongate, usually flattened or thickened, frequently hairy; apex of hind tibia with 2 spurs; thorax hairy; color dark, bluish green; nest generally excavated in soft wood; larvae fed pollen and honey; widespread, generally about flowers; solitary.

Bumble Bees (Family Apidae, Subfamily Apinae)—some body hairs, generally including those on thorax, branched or feathery; pronotum like sphecid wasps; 1st segment of hind tarsus elongate, usually flattened or thickened, frequently hairy; apex of hind tibia with 2 spurs; very hairy, hair color generally black with yellow patches on thorax and/or abdomen; only social bees besides honey bees; 3 castes, queens, workers, and drones; nest in ground, only queens survive fall and overwinter, first spring brood all workers (sterile females) which perform all colony work except reproduction, drones (male reproductives) and more queens produced in late summer; larvae fed pollen and honey; adults widespread, generally around flowers; includes a group of parasitic bees that lack a worker caste, queens lay eggs in the nests of other bumble bees.

Honey Bees (Family Apidae, Subfamily Apinae)—some body hairs, generally including those on thorax, branched or feathery; pronotum like sphecid wasps; 1st segment of hind tarsus elongate, usually flattened or thickened, frequently hairy; neither tibial spurs nor lobe on rear margin of hind wing; only social bees besides bumble bees; a single, introduced species, generally living in man-made hives; possess same castes as bumble bees; swarms including a new queen are necessary to start a new colony; larvae fed pollen and honey.

ECHINODERMATA (SPINY-SKINNED ANIMALS)

Diagnosis: body unsegmented, usually radially symmetrical and 5-parted in adults; includes starfishes, brittle stars, sea urchins, sand dollars, sea lilies, sea cucumbers, and their allies, animals generally unique in appearance; generally biparental, egg to 1 or 2 larval stages to adult.
Habitat: strictly marine.

SUBPHYLUM PELMATOZOA

Diagnosis: attached during part or all of life by the end opposite the mouth, attachment either direct or by a stalk; both mouth and anus are on the upper surface; body in a cuplike skeleton (calyx); 5 classes, 4 entirely extinct.

Class Crinoidea (Sea Lilies and Feather Stars

Diagnosis: calyx symmetrical; arms 5, branching at base (superficially appearing as 10 arms); tube feet lack suckers, tentaclelike, food collecting; most to all filter feeders, some may be detritus feeders; 1 living order, Articulata.
Sea Lilies (Suborder Isocrinida)—both young and adults attached by a stalk to substrate; deep continental shelf to deep sea.
Feather Stars (Suborder Comatulida)—young stalked and attached, adults break loose from stalk; adults creep along substrate or swim by moving their arms; shallow subtidal to deep sea.

SUBPHYLUM ELEUTHEROZOA

Diagnosis: free-living, stalkless; anus, if present, on side opposite mouth; structure regularly 5-armed or -rayed; 5 classes, only 1 entirely extinct.

Class Holothuroidea (Sea Cucumbers)

Diagnosis: body elongate, soft or 5-sided, without spines, sometimes wormlike, generally cucumberlike; mouth surrounded by tentacles; arms absent; most live on or under rocks and in or on sand and mud; plankton trapped by the mucous-covered tentacles, or bottom debris taken into body, organic matter being used as food; partial self-destruction frequently results when animals are irritated, destroyed parts are regenerated; some have a posterior group of mucous-covered tubes that are thrust out to entrap food or entangle an enemy.

SEA LILIES-FEATHER STARS

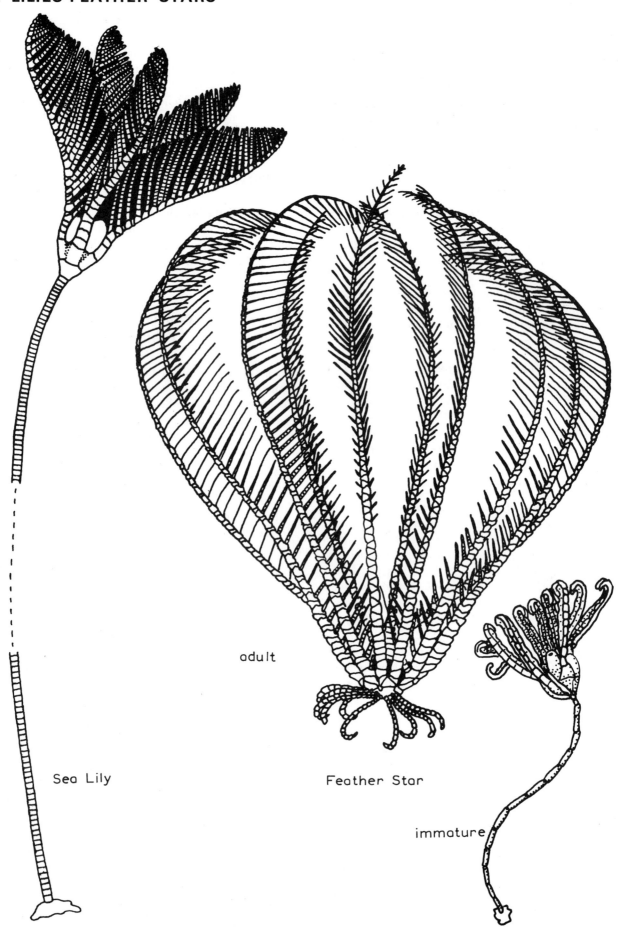

Sea Lily

adult

Feather Star

immature

SEA CUCUMBERS

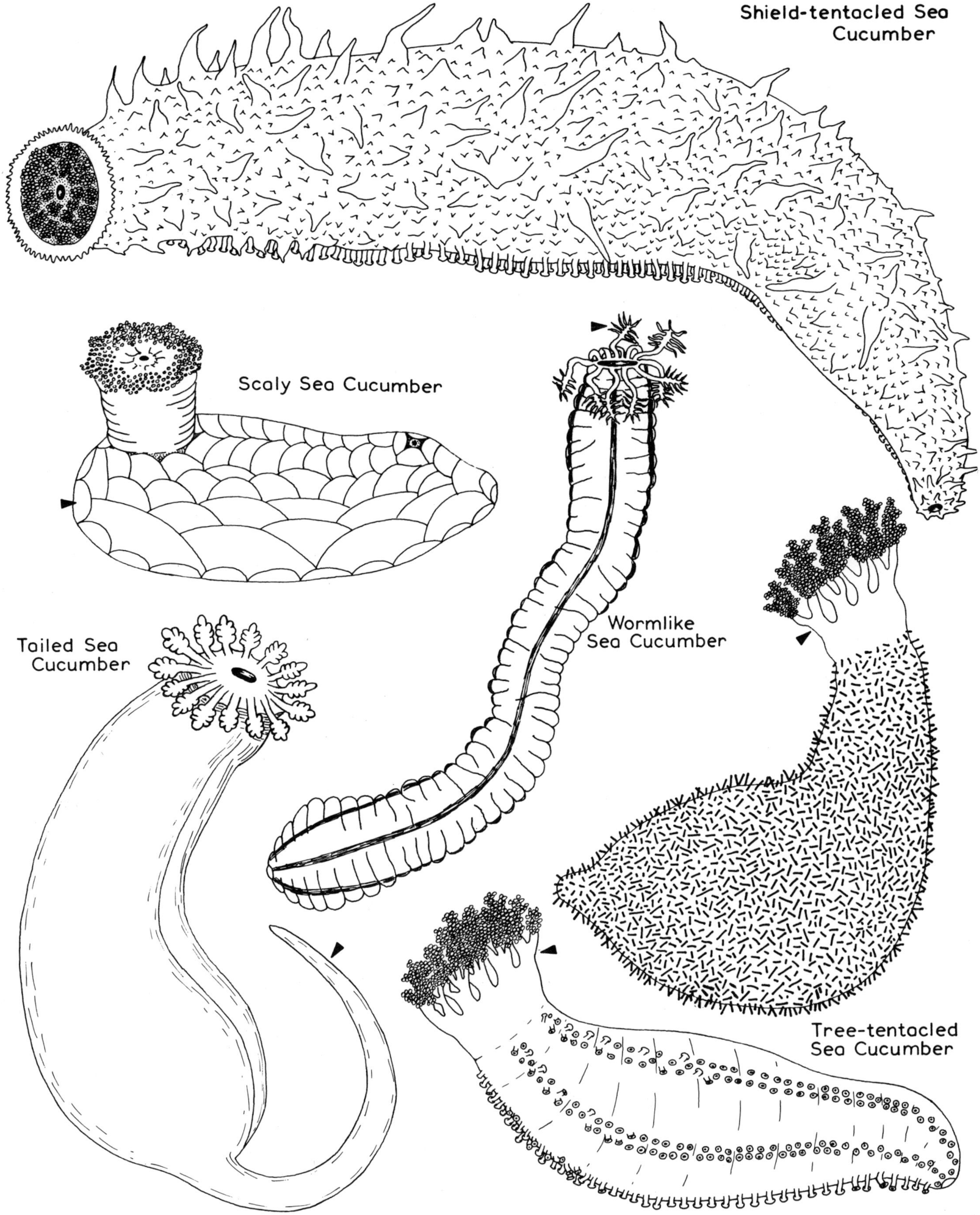

Shield-tentacled Sea Cucumber

Scaly Sea Cucumber

Wormlike Sea Cucumber

Tailed Sea Cucumber

Tree-tentacled Sea Cucumber

Pelagic Sea Cucumbers (Order Elasipoda)—resemble shield-tentacled sea cucumbers; tentacles having shield-shaped ends but mouth opens downward; tube feet present; pelagic from surface to about 2-mile depths, perhaps also on bottom.

Shield-Tentacled Sea Cucumbers (Order Aspidochoria)—resemble pelagic sea cucumbers; tentacles having shield-shaped ends but mouth opens forward; tube feet present; intertidal to deep water.

Scaly or Creeping Sea Cucumbers (Order Dendrochirota, Family Psolidae)—tentacles follow a treelike branching pattern; body more-or-less flattened with a well-defined ventral sole, top and sides covered with scales; tube feet present; lowest intertidal to edge of continental shelf.

Tree-Tentacled Sea Cucumbers (Order Dendrochirota, Family Cucumariidae)—tentacles follow a treelike branching pattern; body neither flattened nor covered with scales; tube feet present; intertidal to moderate depths, about 1 mile.

Tailed Sea Cucumbers (Order Molpadonia)—tentacles finger-shaped with or without lateral knobs or lobes; body terminated by a tail; tube feet absent; shallow subtidal to moderate depths, about 1 mile.

Wormlike Sea Cucumbers (Order Apoda)—tentacles featherlike; tube feet absent; body elongate; intertidal to deep continental shelf.

Class Echinoidea (Sea Urchins, Sea Biscuits, and Sand Dollars)

Diagnosis: body globular (sea urchins); heart-shaped (heart urchins), oval to pear-shaped (pear urchins), or disc-shaped (sand dollars), covered by movable spines; no tentacles around mouth; arms absent; most often seen along rocky shores in holes in rock, others occur on the ocean floor in bays or other shallow coastal waters, some are washed ashore or are in holdfasts of kelp that have been washed ashore; variable diet of seaweeds, dead animal remains, small organisms, and organic matter contained in ingested sand or mud.

Clubbed Sea Urchins (Order Cidaroidea)—body globular, spherical or flattened; large spines, heavy, blunt at tip, each large spine encircled by distinct, small spines; shallow Atlantic southern waters, north to Carolinas.

Spiny Sea Urchins (Order Diadematoidea)—body globular; large spines sharp at tip or thin, smaller spines tend to be in rows as are large spines and are not greatly smaller than large spines; intertidal to deep waters, rocky and sandy bottoms.

Sea Biscuits or Cake Urchins (Order Clypeastroidea, Family Clypeastridae)—body globular, somewhat flattened but not disclike; spines short; mouth centrally located on underside; petal-like design on top of skeleton; Atlantic intertidal and shallow subtidal, generally on sandy bottoms.

Sand Dollars (Order Clypeastroidea, Family Scutellidae)—body disclike; spines short; mouth centrally located on underside; petal-like design on top of skeleton; very shallow subtidal to edge of continental shelf, sandy bottoms.

Keyhole Urchins or Sand Dollars (Order Clypeastroidea, Family Scutellidae)—body disclike with a central slitlike hole and marginal slitlike holes or deep notches; spines short; mouth centrally located on underside; petal-like design on top of skeleton; very shallow Atlantic subtidal to edge of continental shelf, sandy bottoms.

Pear Urchins (Order Cassiduloidea)—body somewhat elongate, oval to pear-shaped, front end rounded, without anterior notch; spines short; mouth on top; no petal-like design; continental shelf and slope.

Heart Urchins (Order Spatangoidea)—body somewhat elongate, oval to pear- or heart-shaped, front end with a notch; spines short; mouth toward front of underside of body; petal-like design on top of skeleton, generally hidden by spines; muddy or sandy bottoms of bays and continental shelf.

Class Asteroidea (Sea Stars or Starfishes)

Diagnosis: body star-shaped, generally 5 or multiples of 5 "arms;" underside of each arm (mouth or oral surface) with a deep logitudinal groove containing tube feet; usually seen attached to intertidal rocks, also on sandy and muddy bottoms of bays, estuaries, and the deep ocean; mostly carnivorous, preying on mollusks, also scavengers.

Order Phanerozonia

Diagnosis: arms with 2 rows or marginal plates or spines that form an edge to the arm (see leather star); tube feet in 2 rows.

Sand Stars (Family Astropectinidae)—tube feet pointed, without a definite flat sucking disc but each may have a small pointed knob at the tip; marginal plates present.

Active Stars (Family Luidiidae)—tube feet pointed, without a definite flat sucking disc but each may have a small pointed knob at the tip; marginal plates replaced by spines.

Subtidal Stars (Family Goniasteridae)—tube feet with well-developed sucking discs; marginal plates large, clearly visible; subtidal, accidental in intertidal areas.

Irregular Stars (Family Linckiidae)—tube feet with well-developed sucking discs; marginal plates small, somewhat obscure; arms irregular, unequal in length.

Leather Stars (Family Asteropidae)—tube feet with well-developed sucking discs; marginal plates small, generally hidden by thick, smooth, tough skin which covers entire body.

Order Spinulosa

Diagnosis: marginal plates inconspicuous; tube feet in 2 rows (rarely 4 in very deep water forms).

SEA URCHINS-SEA BISCUITS-SAND DOLLARS

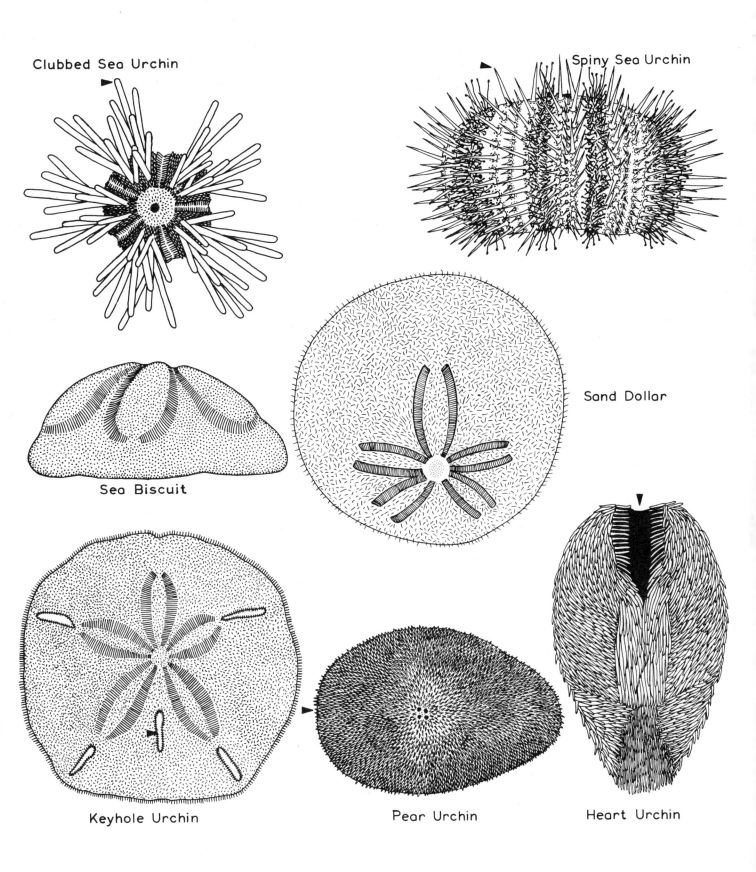

Clubbed Sea Urchin

Spiny Sea Urchin

Sea Biscuit

Sand Dollar

Keyhole Urchin

Pear Urchin

Heart Urchin

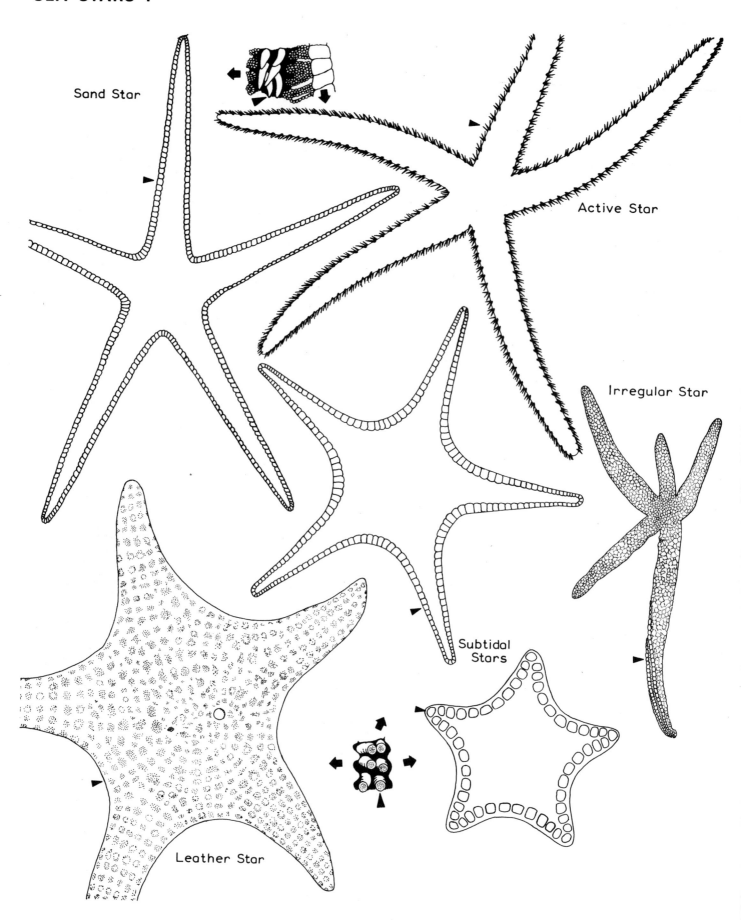

Sand Star

Active Star

Irregular Star

Subtidal Stars

Leather Star

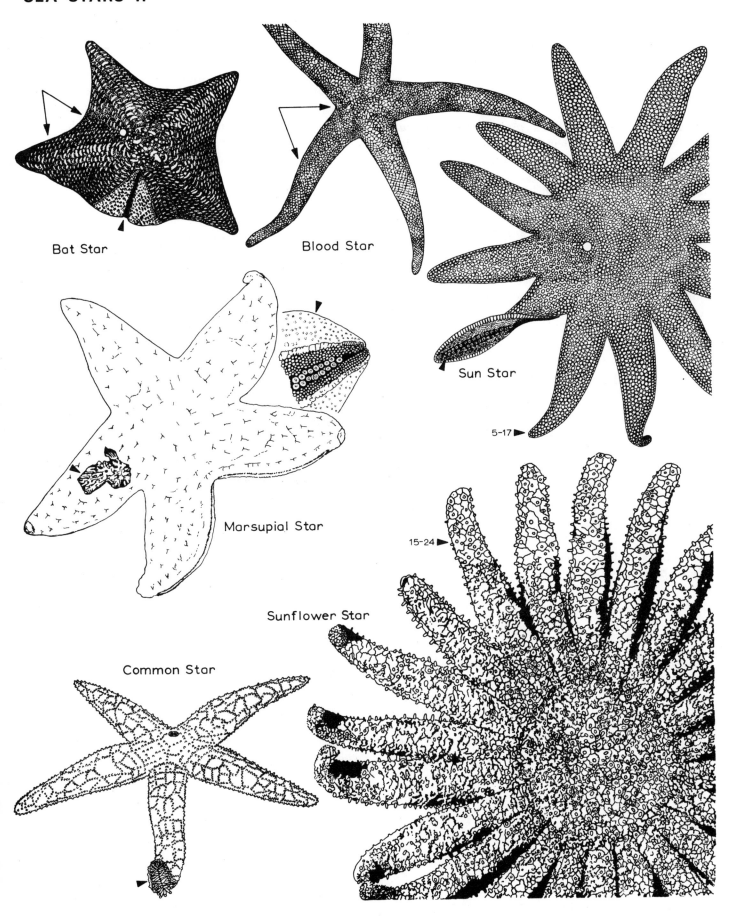

Bat Star

Blood Star

Sun Star

5-17 ▶

Marsupial Star

15-24 ▶

Sunflower Star

Common Star

Bat Stars (Family Asterinidae)—groove containing tube feet narrow; body pentagonal, central disc diameter greater than arm length.

Blood Stars (Family Echinasteridae)—groove containing tube feet narrow; central disc diameter about 1/2 arm length; color generally red.

Sun Stars (Family Solasteridae)—groove containing tube feet broad; without fins.

Marsupial or Pouched Stars (Family Pterasteridae)—groove containing tube feet broad; edge of body with a finlike membrane; upper surface covered by a membrane supported by circlets of long, slender spines, cavity formed serving as a brood pouch.

Order Forcipulata

Diagnosis: marginal plates inconspicuous; tube feet in 4 rows.

Sunflower Stars (Family Asteriidae)—arms 15–24.

Common Stars (Family Asteriidae)—arms generally 5–8, less than 15.

Class Ophiuroidea
(Brittle and Basket Stars)

Diagnosis: body star-shaped but arms sharply marked off from a central disc; generally 5 arms; without longitudinal grooves on underside of arms, or with grooves covered by small plates; intertidal (basket star not likely in Pacific) to over 1-mile depths, brittle stars common in cracks and crevices or under objects in tidepools; feed on small animals, especially crustaceans and mollusks; cast off part to all of 1 or more arms to distract predators, regenerate lost parts.

Brittle Stars (Order Ophiurae)—arms never branched.

Basket Stars (Order Euryalae)—arms branched.

CHAETOGNATHA (ARROW WORMS)

Diagnosis: body unsegmented, wormlike, transparent, torpedo-shaped; head with characteristic bristles surrounding the mouth; body with lateral and tail fins; feed on microorganisms; hermaphroditic, egg to stage resembling adult.

Habitat: strictly marine; mostly pelagic, deep water during the day, surface at night, also attached to algae or rocks in shallow water.

HEMICHORDATA
(ACORN WORMS)

Diagnosis: body unsegmented, wormlike, fleshy, and contractile; snout cylindrical but drawn to a blunt point, short or long, somewhat tongue- or acornlike; collar cylindrical, usually as wide as long; trunk elongate, with numerous paired gill slits entering pharynx; filter feed by burrowing with mouth open; when water, sand, mud, and organic matter reach pharynx, water is expelled; after organic matter is digested and assimilated, sand, mud, and undigested organic matter is expelled through the anus; biparental, larva resembles that of some echinoderms.

Habitat: strictly marine, mostly intertidal; either form burrows or live under rocks, in rock cavities, or among algae, but also at some depth.

POGONOPHORA
(BEARD WORMS)

Diagnosis: body unsegmented, wormlike; 3 body regions consisting of 1 to many tentacles on the anterior region, a weakly defined collar, and a trunk; no digestive system or gill slits; believed to capture food with their tentacles and digest it while it is held by the tentacles; probably no larval stage.

Habitat: strictly marine, mostly very deep sea tube dwellers, some in shallow water; known forms almost entirely from Northern Hemisphere, closest from Central America.

CHORDATA (CHORDATES)

Diagnosis: body segmented but may not be visible externally; a highly variable group as adults (see diagnoses below); includes the subphylum Vertebrata (vertebrates excluded from this book); invertebrate chordates strictly marine; hermaphroditic or biparental, egg to larva to adult.

SUBPHYLUM CEPHALOCHORDATA (Lancets)

Diagnosis: fishlike but simple-structured, without fins; gills generally involved in filter feeding; sexes separate; shallow water, sand dwellers, but some are intertidal; at low tide, lancets may jump out of and back into sand when disturbed.

SUBPHYLUM TUNICATA (Urochordata) (Tunicates)

Diagnosis: body form variable, tadpolelike, cask- or spindle-shaped, or varying from flat sheets to irregularly lobed masses to globular, saclike or clublike individuals, specifics below.

BRITTLE STARS-BASKET STARS

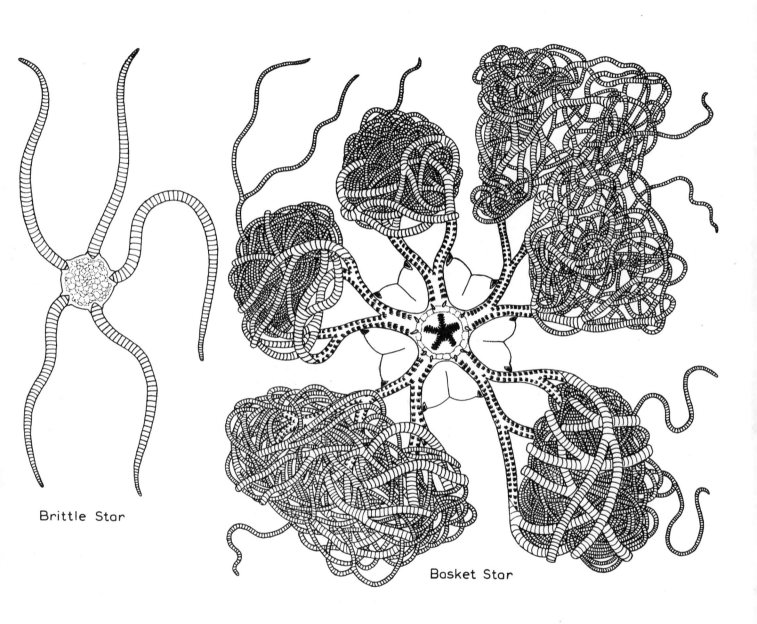

Brittle Star

Basket Star

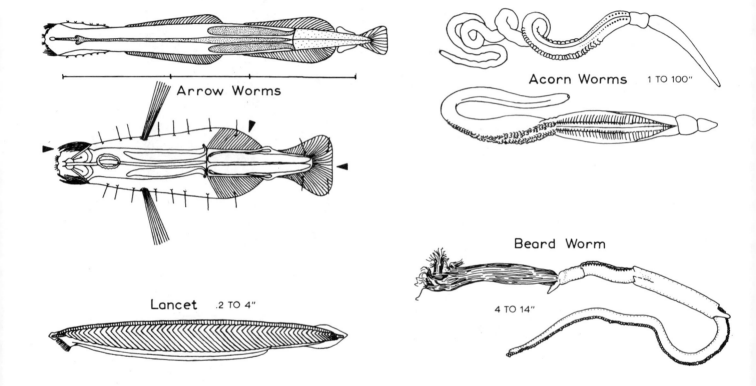

Arrow Worms

Acorn Worms   1 TO 100"

Beard Worm

4 TO 14"

Lancet   .2 TO 4"

PELAGIC TUNICATE LIFE CYCLE

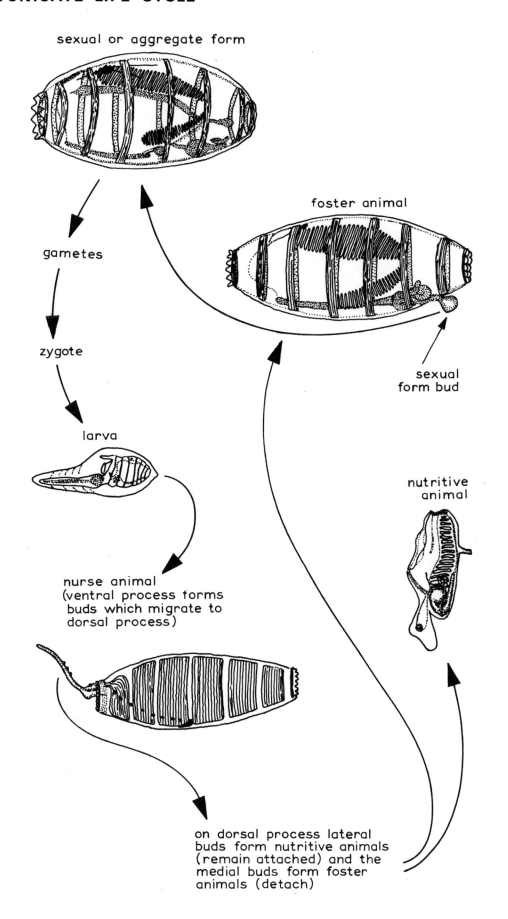

sexual or aggregate form

gametes

zygote

larva

foster animal

sexual
form bud

nutritive
animal

nurse animal
(ventral process forms
buds which migrate to
dorsal process)

on dorsal process lateral
buds form nutritive animals
(remain attached) and the
medial buds form foster
animals (detach)

Class Larvaceae
(Larvaceans or Tadpole Tunicates)

Diagnosis: mostly minute, transparent, tadpolelike tunicates of persistent larval form, free-swimming marine plankton that have a jellylike tunic they may leave to secrete a new one; microscopic food is filtered by tunic structures, the necessary water current for filtering being produced by moving the tail; usually hermaphroditic, but with cross-fertilization, individuals first functioning as males and then as females; open ocean forms.

Class Thaliaceae
(Pelagic Tunicates and Sea Thimbles)

Diagnosis: conspicuous forms a few inches long but colonies much longer; body casklike, spindle-like, or thimble-like.

Pelagic or Chain Tunicates (Orders Salpida and Diliolida)—body casklike or spindle-like with anterior and posterior openings, ringed by muscles that may provide contractions necessary for jet-propelled swimming, others transported only by currents; body form generally changes in relation to a complex life cycle (see accompanying figure), sexual forms hermaphroditic; filter feeders on microscopic life; open ocean forms; Salpida cylindrical or prism-shaped with muscle bands incomplete below, Doliolida (shown only in life cycle plate) casklike with 8 complete muscle rings.

Sea Thimbles (Order Pyrosomida)—body shape somewhat resembling an elongate thimble; colonial, individuals with incurrent openings on outside and excurrent openings on the inside; sudden body contraction forces water out of open end of "thimble" jet propelling animal through water; body transparent, pink or colorless, luminescent; relatively rare, pelagic but sometimes washed ashore.

Class Ascidiaceae (Ascidians)

Diagnosis: variable in size and shape; tunic usually gelatinous, sometimes cellulose; organisms individual, colonial, or compound; compound type distinguished from other types by many individuals being in a single, gelatinous tunic (individual of a compound type shown with sea blubbers); compound types include sea mushrooms and sea blubbers.

Sea Squirts—body more-or-less saclike; solitary; body transparent and often appearing fragile to opaque and heavy; often squirt water through excurrent opening, incurrent and excurrent openings generally on projections of tunic; intertidal to moderate depths, attached.

Solitary Sea Clubs—body more-or-less clublike with incurrent and excurrent openings on projections of tunic; body covering heavy, generally wrinkled, sometimes spiny; solitary; frequently and abruptly eject water when disturbed as do sea squirts; intertidal to moderate depths, attached.

Colonial Sea Clubs—individuals clublike; colonial, individuals connected at bases by stemlike structures; generally transparent to semitransparent, body covering gelatinous; intertidal to moderate depths, attached.

Sea Grapes—individuals saclike as are sea squirts, also transparent; colonial, individuals connected at bases by stemlike structures; intertidal to moderate depths, attached.

Sea Blubbers—compound, individuals grouped about and sharing a common excurrent opening (considerably larger than incurrent openings), many such organizations of individuals per single mass of these ascidians; masses variable, range from thin, flat sheets to groups of stalked, tall, irregular lobes (lobes sometimes tongue-, club-, or handlike); intertidal to moderate depths.

Sea Mushrooms—compound, individuals grouped about and sharing a common excurrent opening; mushroom-shaped (the same species assumes other body shapes of the sea blubber type); intertidal to moderate depths.

TUNICATES

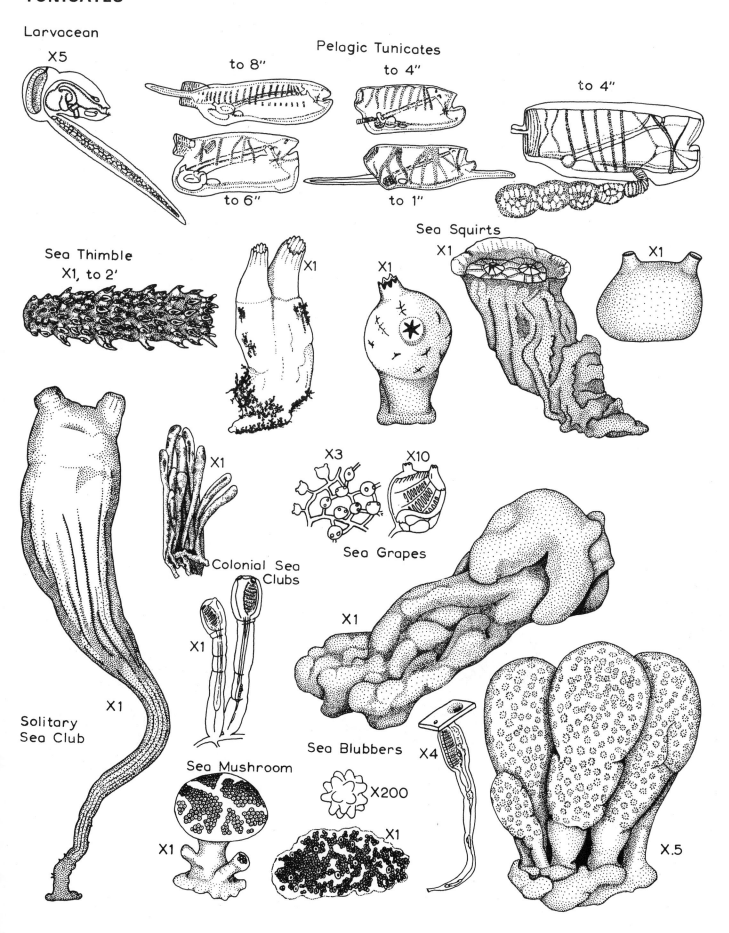

Larvacean
X5

Pelagic Tunicates
to 8"
to 4"
to 4"
to 6"
to 1"

Sea Thimble
X1, to 2'

Sea Squirts
X1
X1
X1
X1

X1

X3
X10
Sea Grapes

X1

Colonial Sea
Clubs
X1

X1

X1

Solitary
Sea Club
X1

Sea Mushroom

Sea Blubbers
X4
X200

X1

X1

X.5

INDEX